THE ILLUSTRATED

HERBAL ENCYCLOPEDIA

BRENDA LITTLE

This paperback edition printed in 2007

ISBN 978-86147-067-6

7 9 10 8 6

Published by ABBEYDALE PRESS
An imprint of Bookmart Limited
Registered Number 2372865
Blaby Road, Wigston
Leicestershire LE18 4SE
England

Produced for Bookmart Limited by
Carrawong Books
P.O. Box 612
Turramurra, NSW 2074
Australia

Editorial director: Anthony Macdougall
Photography: David Liddle, Andrew Kay, Romeo Viligno
Consultant–Teas and Infusions: Daniela di Marchi
Consultant–Craft & Decorating: Winsome Mc Pherson
Consultant–Massage: Eva Papadopoulo
Consultant–Home Brewing: James Lusby
Designer: J. Harvey Hapi
Artwork: Harvey Graphic Design

Acknowledgements
The author and producers would like to thank the following for their contributions:
Andrew Kay, Bob & Anne-Marie Magnus–The Magnus Gardens, Lynne Brown–Common Scents, Horden House, Jackie Creacy, Jimmy Wells, Jill Gatty–The Fragrant Garden, Judy Madden, Karen Green, Kim Fletcher, Louise Earwacker, Libby & Greg Moulder–Highland Herbs, Rachel Howell, Rob & Jean Bates.

Important Notice
Herbs are very powerful healing tools. If they are misused, they can be harmful. This book is not a medical reference book. The advice it contains is general, not specific and neither the author nor the publishers can be held responsible for any adverse reactions to the recipes, formulas, recommendations or instructions contained herein. Before trying any herbal formula, sample a small quantity first in case you have any adverse or allergic reaction. Do not try self-diagnosis or attempt self-treatment for serious or long term problems without consulting a qualified medical herbalist. Do not take herbal remedies if you are undergoing any other course of medical treatment without seeking professional advice.

Printed in Thailand

CONTENTS

Introduction

There is something beguiling about herbs—friendly and undemanding, fresh and fragrant, they romp through a garden, good companions to us whether we are sick or well. Whatever the situation you can be sure there is a green friend able to offer comfort and possible cure.

Apart from their helpfulness, herbs have wonderful social graces. Many of us must have been poignantly reminded of childhood, by the sudden whiff of lavender from an opened cupboard or of lost love by the warm breath of crushed leaves. Smell is the most sensual of our senses and the fragrance of herbs enables us to indulge it to the full.

The scent of food cooking—the lingering presence of thyme on the air when the kitchen is closed for the night—the clean and wholesome waft of air from the incense cup where pine or rosemary is burning—the spicy clove breath of a pomander—the sweet fresh smell of a lime-scented drawer—how can we resist the pleasures herbs can bring us?

For the nimble-fingered there are projects galore—making herbal incense, scented candles, pot pourri, dried bouquets, herbal paper, room deodorisers, wreaths and sachets—for the culinary minded not only can herbs be used in cooking but in the making of teas and wine! Once you become interested in herbs a whole world opens up—green, clean, natural and endlessly rewarding.

Man has been learning about the plants which share his environment from his earliest days and though the accumulated knowledge is voluminous it is still sketchy. It is estimated that there are at least half a million species of plant in the world but only about ten per cent of the organic constituents have been identified. Linnaeus said "What we know of the Divine works is much fewer than those of which we are ignorant," and his words are as true today as they were 200 years ago—and still we destroy the rain forests which are so full of unknown potential for the good of us all. Man is a woefully slow learner.

Knowledge has come slowly. For primitive man the ability to make use of wild plants involved the long, slow process of trial and error—judgement of the properties of a plant was based on the observation of its appearance, scent

Useful culinary and medicinal herbs such as the hardy Curry plant (Helichrysum italicum), Thyme (Thymus vulgaris), and Lavender (Lavendula hidcote), are often overlooked for their picturesque and attractive landscaping qualities.

and habit of growth and on the superstitions which had grown up round it. By the time the early civilizations had learned how to capture information by inscribing characters on tablets or papyri they could list around a thousand plants which were useful to man.

The earliest paper manuscript to list and illustrate herbs that we still have is DE MATERIA MEDICA, written by the Greek Dioscorides in the first century AD and illustrated with beautiful water-colours more than four hundred years later. This book became the "bible" for those wishing to use herbs for healing and remained so until well into the seventeenth century when knowledge of the plant world became more detailed wide-spread and understood.

Today synthetic drugs have largely ousted the natural medicines as the popular way of healing but will these drugs still be around a thousand years from now, one wonders. Thyme will still be a powerful antiseptic and angelica will still ease flatulence and herbal medicines will still not cause the iatrogenic illnesses suffered by patients treated with synthetic drugs. We will probably never be able to meet all the medical needs of the world with natural medicines but our well-being can be greatly increased by knowledge of how the plants used by our forefathers can still help us.

Herbal medicine does not have the dramatic effect of modern drugs but neither does it have the horrific side-effects some can produce. Today's cure is never tomorrow's nightmare. The medicinal properties of herbs have years of sustained proof both of their safety and their efficacy—often many thousands of years—and patience will pay off.

Cure or healing may come more slowly than one would like but it will be natural and trouble-free. Conditions which have taken years to build up will take time to correct so, in most cases, it is as well to settle down to a three month course of treatment. Drastic illness demands emergency treatment—and professional help should be sought without delay, but for complaints that present no large, immediate threat the herbal remedy could be the answer. Herbs cleanse the body of toxins while treating the malady—antibiotics treat the malady but leave their poisons in the body. The safest way may be the slowest but surely it is worthwhile.

It cannot be too strongly stressed that this is a layman's book with information culled over a long period of years and all of it has proved useful to somebody at some time, but it is no substitute for the services of doctor, herbalist or homeopathic practitioner with long years of study and experience to call on. A book of this nature must not attempt to usurp professional advice—all it can do is to help widen knowledge and stimulate interest. Understanding is of vital importance in every sphere of life; taking the trouble to understand how herbs can be of use to us in so many different ways could be one of the most important steps we take.

Growing herbs is easy and enjoyable; their use is simple. But this simplicity should never be thought of as unimportant or insignificant for it has the enduring quality of all great truths. No matter how clever man may be he will always find that, in the last analysis, he is totally dependent on Nature. And Nature is bountiful. A new recognition of both that dependence and bounty has been steadily growing in the general public and science is showing a new interest in medical botany—we may find that ignorance of the Divine works that Linnaeus wrote about will lessen more quickly than could have been hoped.

In the meantime there is much to do in pleasurable ways—quite apart from their serious role in our lives, herbs can be the source of fun and enjoyment and many hours of quiet content.

Above: *Many early books on herbs were printed on Caxton hand presses with woodcut illustrations.*

Opposite *A herbal garden can be both colourful and fragrant.*

Herbs
in the
Garden

Herb Garden Design

Herbs are not only rewarding they are also beautiful, useful and often fragrant. They do not demand constant attention, are good friends to other plants and lend themselves easily to individual designs.

Herbs are pleasantly informal plants, given the chance they will sprawl and spread and wander. If you are planning a formal herb garden you will have to keep your eye on them.

Herbs can be used in many different ways. They can be a world unto themselves in their own garden or they can mix with flowers in a border or vegetables in a bed.

One of the most attractive gardens I know has herbs, flowers and vegetables growing all together in delightful profusion. It belongs to a very relaxed gardener who believes that Nature is a better designer than we are. It has a wonderful careless beauty but finding a herb in a hurry is something of a problem.

If space is limited growing herbs in the flower-beds can be the answer. Tall upright perennials like golden rod, lovage and angelica take their place quite happily among other tall plants at the back of the border and low-growing, spreading catmint, chamomile and thyme make a pleasant front edging.

Well-trimmed lavender, rosemary and sage bushes can border paths leading through the flower garden, their grey-green leaves a soft contrast to the brighter colours. But there is the likelihood that herbs in the border will become just faces in the crowd—it is better to give them a bed of their own.

Achillea millefolium, the common yarrow, has many colourful variations and softens the formality of a traditional herb garden.

MARKING OUT DESIGNS

Marking out a design is not difficult.

A peg hammered into the ground with a pencil tied to a measured piece of string attached to it will enable circles and loops to be scratched into the soil. They can then be outlined with small pebbles to see if the effect is pleasing and modified if it isn't.

EDGINGS

The dwarf hedging popular in the old days was box and it is still a good choice because the constant trimming necessary to keep it between 17 cm/7 inches and 24 cm/10 inches high does not ruin its looks. Bear the trimming in mind when choosing the borders.

Thyme can look very neat. Rosemary, santolina and lavender are possible choices too—but discuss the properties of the varieties chosen with your nurseryman to make sure you have chosen a suitable one for they are vigorous growers.

As can be seen it takes a lot of plants to outline the design of the garden so forward planning is necessary. To buy small growing plants would be very expensive so cuttings are the best bet. You can grow them in pots in readiness or plan out your design in the garden and set out the cuttings at about 10 cm/4 inch intervals. Extra cuttings growing in pots will be a back-up supply in case some don't take.

The thing to remember about a knot garden is that every plant will need pruning and clipping to keep in shape.

If you're not prepared to give the knot garden close and loving attention it is better not to bother. There are no half measures—its beauty comes at a price.

KNOT GARDENS

The amount of space and time that can be given to herbs will largely determine the choice of how to grow them. For an enthusiastic gardener with plenty of both there will be much joy in making a herb garden which follows the traditions of centuries long gone. The knot garden however demands a discipline and attention few of today's gardeners can achieve and the ordered look which stresses the control man exercises over Nature does not appeal to everybody.

The design of a knot garden is based on clearly defined shapes—loops, circles, triangles, squares, bordered by a very neatly clipped edging. The more complicated the design the more work is needed, for if the edgings are allowed to become straggly the clarity and virtue of the design is lost.

One can, of course, make one's own

A wide variety of design of knot gardens can be achieved but the basic concept must be one of geometric symmetry. In their Elizabethan heyday the patterns had delightful names such as cinquefoil, trefoyle, crossbow and flower-de-luce, and were often formed of intricately twisted designs. Today simpler patterns are preferred but the use of compact plants to achieve the general effect cannot be over-emphasised. A level site must be chosen and the smaller the area the simpler the design must be. Some spaces can be filled with shells or coloured pebbles to provide a permanent foil for a range of plants.

1 Crossbow; 2 New knot; 3 Curious fine knot; 4 New knot for a perfect garden; 5 Flower-de-luce; 6 trefoyle; 7 Flower de luce; 8 A Good pattern for a Quarter of herbs.

Thymus.sp. are hardy and useful for path edges, quite able to bear the odd footprint.

HERBS FOR LOW BORDERS AND EDGING

boxwood
chamomile
chives
dwarf of bush basil
dwarf rosemary
dwarf sage
hyssop
parsley
santolina
savory
thyme

design—keeping it simple because modern life does not leave much time, for taking care, but keeping the "feel" of the traditions.

A simple knot garden

A very simple design, but one which will nevertheless take time to establish and be seen at its full beauty, is a square bed bordered with a medium height lavender or rosemary hedge.

In the centre of the bed is a feature—a statue, a sundial, a large flowering plant in a pot—anything which pleases you and draws the eye. Large loops of figures of eight are north and south of the bed, smaller ones to the east and west. The paths are clean and clear.

The loops can be outlined by low-growing, small-leafed perennial herbs—and larger ones within the loops.

Colour can be introduced by herbs in flower or with variegated foliage. The contrasting leaf colours of herbs give interest to any design and there are a range of colours within a species that can be exploited. Thyme varieties range from the dark green to the variegated.

SCENTED HERBS

Lemon
lemon balm, lemon thyme, lemon verbena

Sweet
angelica, balm, bergamot burnet, catmint, chamomile, dill, fennel, hyssop, lavender, lovage, marjoram, pennyroyal, rosemary, sage, tansy, thyme, woodruff, yarrow

Spicy
anise, basil, caraway, coriander, mint, pennyroyal

Distinctive
eau-de-cologne mint, tarragon, wormwood

Spreading herbs can be a nuisance in a design like this—if there is one you must use, trim the roots before planting.

A chequer-board design

Paving runs diagonally across the grey squares. Each coloured square is planted with a different herb.

FORMAL GARDENS

Circular planting

You will have to work hard at this one too but the effects can be magical—it is a real challenge for the artistic gardener. Perennial plants only should be used.

The hub of the design should be a tall plant—the herbs growing in circles round it should be of gradually decreasing size. The outer border surrounding the circle should be of neat, low-growing herbs. Green leaves, grey-green and silver leaves, the rich red of bergamot, the quiet mauve of lavender, the clean yellow of the button flowers of santolina and tansy and the white simplicity of the daisy-like flowers of chamomile offer a pallette of colour and a wide range of use.

A simple wheel design

An old wheel gives a ready-made design ready for planting. The spokes can be painted white to define the pattern and herbs of different sorts planted between them to make a circular whirl of different coloured leaves and flowers.

Ladder planting

This design is very simple. The plot is rectangular and paths are the rungs of the ladder.

For a good design make the length of the plot at least one third greater than the width. This design suits the busy cook who can rush into the garden and have no difficulty in either finding the needed herb or reaching it easily.

A more elaborate design

Mark out a square—make a smallish circle in the centre.

Mark off triangular beds in each of

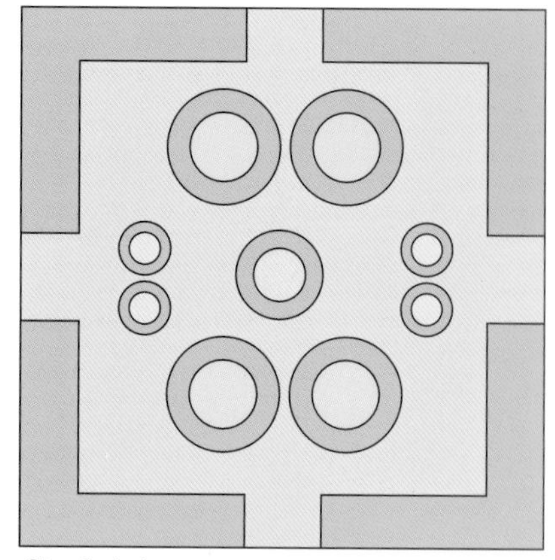
Simple design.

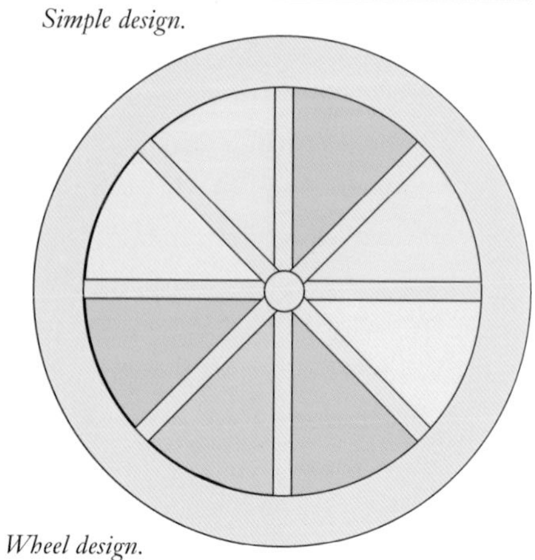
Wheel design.

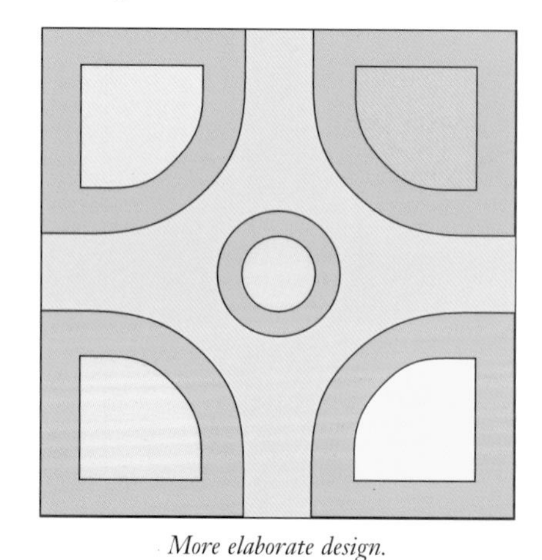
More elaborate design.

Ladder design.

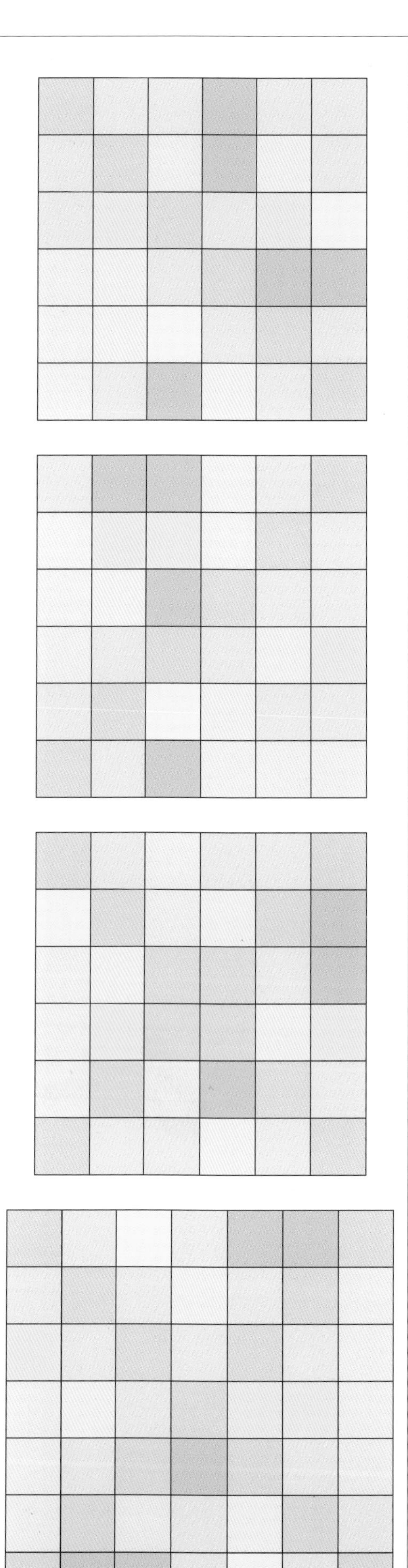

Chequerboard designs.

the four corners leaving a space for entrance into the centre on each of the four sides.

The curved shape of the bottom of the triangles softens the angularity of the design. The paths can be paved or laid with gravel.

Little plants of creeping thyme tucked in between the flags will give scent underfoot.

Though there are five planting areas there is still space for a deck-chair from which the bees and butterflies hovering over the plantings of sweet herbs can be lazily enjoyed.

Above: Yarrow, lavender and wormwood (Artemesia absinthium), a rambling mass of colour.

INFORMAL GARDENS

An informal garden does not take much looking after but some control is necessary if the faster-growing herbs are not to take over. Informality works best on a large scale where the lushness and vigour of the herbs can be given full rein and they can self-seed happily.

A sunny bank is ideal. The herbs are planted close together—graded in height and width and left to see how they go. Encroachment can be gently discouraged as they grow. Unless you are really familiar with the appearance of each of the herbs planted it can sometimes be difficult to tell which is which without tasting them—but that is no hardship.

Planning an informal garden

The first thing is to decide which herbs you want to grow. There are a number of herbs no garden should be without—sage and thyme, lavender and rosemary, mint and parsley.

The decision about mint and parsley is easy—they need separate beds. Mints like a slightly richer soil than most herbs and certainly need more water. They are invasive and have to be strictly controlled. If growing more than one variety of mint keep them well apart so that they do not cross-pollinate and so lose their individuality.

A small bed, edged with bricks, stones or wood, in the shade, close to the water-tap and the kitchen door is ideal.

Parsley can take more sun and live on less water than mint but it doesn't seem to give of its best in a mixed bed. As a thick border edging, however, it does, and in a bed of its own it will grow strongly and re-seed willingly.

Consider your own habits and needs when planning your garden. Do you plan to use herbs simply as food herbs or do you want a physick garden – as they used to call gardens in which medicinal herbs took pride of place? A cosmetic garden? Are you into craft and decorating? Which herbs will you need and how many?

Plan beds so that the herbs you will need most often are readily accessible.

Plant annual herbs where they will not leave a difficult-to-fill spot when their life is over.

Herbs need sun so don't let tall herbs overshadow small ones. Among the culinary herbs grown for their leaves plant one or two with brightly coloured flowers—santolina, bergamot.

Grow herbs with scented leaves where the leaves are brushed against or are easily reached so that they can be pinched between the fingers to release their perfume.

Beware of the evening primrose, lovely and helpful though it is. Pick the flowers before they go to seed. They make a lot. Forget two or three and there will be a carpet of evening primroses.

RAISED BEDS

A raised bed of culinary herbs near the kitchen door will enable the cook to keep an eye open and ensure that the supply of needed herbs is kept up. Gardening without back-ache is appreciated too and it is nice to have the scents of the plants at face-level.

Planters can be expensive to buy but a handyman could easily knock up a good strong deep box with plenty of drainage holes in the bottom and set it on a bench or any other support that is suitable.

The box need be only an arm's length front to back. It is surprising how many different herbs will grow in a one and a half long metre bed of this depth.

MOUNDED BEDS

If drainage is adequate a mound of soil from 50 cm/20 inches to 1 metre/40 inches high with sloping sides and of any suitable length will do very well if the top is flattened. Planting can be done on the top and down the sides and all the herbs will be within easy reach.

MOUNDING BEDS

1 Make a bottom layer from large rough pieces of rubble—broken bricks, concrete, stone, large pebbles etc.

2 Cover with a mixture of loose gravel mixed with peat and large fibrous plant matter. Chop the matter well and distribute it evenly through the mix and start to shape the mound.

3 Cover with a good depth of friable garden soil, sloping the sides.
If the soil seems too heavy lighten it with some sand or fine gravel.

4 Flatten the top.
The bed can be kept in place with planks, bricks or concrete blocks.

Opposite: *A lovely informal garden.*
Left: *Proud in their mound, chives complement any potager garden.*

HERBS FOR MAKING TEA

angelica, basil, bergamot, borage, catmint, chamomile, golden rod, horehound, jasmine, lemon verbena, lovage, marjoram, mint, parsley, rosemary, sage, sweet cicely, tansy, thyme, woodruff

A GARDEN FOR HONEY BEES

Herbs which attract bees
balm, basil, bergamot, borage, catmint, coltsfoot, fennel, horehound, hyssop, lavender, marjoram, marshmallow, motherwort, rosemary, sage, thyme

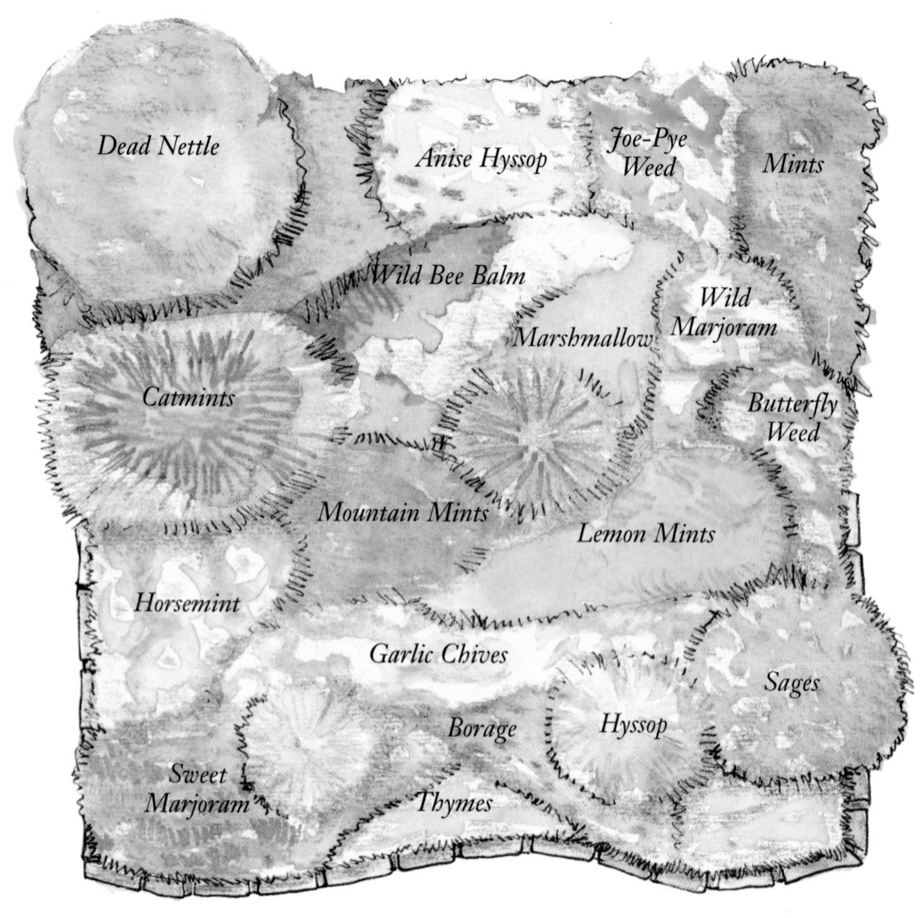

A COOK'S GARDEN

Culinary herbs grown for their leaves

angelica, balm, basil, bay, borage, burnet, chervil, chives, coriander, lovage, marjoram, mint, nasturtium, oregano, parsley, rosemary, sage, tarragon, thyme

A MEDICINAL GARDEN

Garden herbs with medicinal use
agrimony, angelica, anise, balm, bay, burdock, calendula, caraway, centaury, chamomile, chicory, comfrey, dandelion, dill, fennel, garlic, horehound, horseradish, horsetail, lady's mantle, lovage, marjoram, nettle, parsley rosemary, tansy, thyme, yarrow

A FRAGRANT GARDEN

Fragrant herbs to grow
angelica, balm, basil, bay, borage, burnet, chervil, chives, coriander, lovage, marjoram, mint, nasturtium, oregano, parsley, rosemary, sage, tarragon, thyme

Herbs in Containers

Herbs grow very happily in pots and hanging baskets. There are lovely terracotta pots of all shapes and sizes on the market and you can make a spectacular display in the corner of a courtyard or on a balcony.

When you use terracotta pots note that terracotta dries out quickly so an eye must be kept on the water needs of the herbs. Plastic pots inside a better-looking ornamental one can be the answer.

But it doesn't stop there. If you look around you will find all sorts of things to use as containers which can be arranged to make a garden display. Barrels, half-barrels, wine crates, large tins—anything which will contain soil and can provide drainage. Tins will have to have holes punched in the base of course—wooden containers can be drilled.

All old containers pressed into service should be scrubbed well with an equal solution of vinegar and water and then given a good wipe round with a cloth soaked in water containing a small amount of bleach.

The containers should be made to look as attractive as possible of course.

Tins can be painted—the ones in which olive oil is sold are a good size and shape and I have seen them used unpainted, but the lettering and pattern on the tin stops the eye from concentrating on the herbs. A pale unobtrusive grey paint works well.

If you have an old, glazed pot, unsafe to drill, it can be used without drainage holes if extra care in planting is taken.

Put a layer of small pebbles mixed with some charcoal in the bottom of the pot and then fill it with a well-soaked potting mix containing peat and a little vermiculite.

Do not use garden soil. It is not porous enough.

When the plants are growing well take care to keep the soil just lightly moist. The trick is to give time for the water that drains into the pebbles to evaporate before watering again.

A portable mass of colour with geranium, ginger (Zingiber officinale), lemongrass (Cymbopogon citratus), tarragon (Artemesia vulgaris), and lobelia (Lobelio inflata).

There are advantages in having a portable herb garden, You can keep some pots in full sun and others in part-shade—you can move them around if a plant is looking unhappy or you have become bored with the arrangement. Mistakes are more easily put right than when herbs are growing in the garden proper. You may have given only a small space to a herb that has become a favourite and is now being overgrown by its neighbours—the bed is full and extra planting would have to be some distance away. No problem with the pot garden—you just move things round and put in an extra pot. When an annual herb dies down it is quicker to replace it with something fresh than to deal with the one dying in the garden.

Perennial and hardy plants do well year after year in large pots.

HERBS SUITABLE FOR POTS

Large Pots
aloe vera, bay, lavender, lemongrass, rosemary, sage, southernwood, wormwood

Small or Medium Sized Pots
balm, basil, calendula, chives, marjoram, mint, oregano, parsley, sage, thyme

Left: *Annuals and salad herbs do well in small pots.*

Below: *Choose prostrate or green-leaved herbs for hanging baskets. Contrasting foliage looks good all year round.*

HANGING BASKETS

Herbs in hanging baskets can be a very attractive sight.

Hung at different heights, some baskets containing a profusion of just one herb, others full of herbs that contrast with each other in shape and shades of colour, make a garden in the air.

Growing herbs in hanging baskets is less expensive than growing them in pots or containers which are often important to the effect created, whereas the container for a hanging garden is only important for the function it fulfils and can remain unseen.

Before starting to make the baskets, consider all the practicalities.

Watering hanging baskets can present problems. They drip.

Outdoors that may not matter—indoors it could. No matter how lovely a container, test it for weight before you plant it up. Because of the dripping you might have to take it down and water it elsewhere. Lifting a heavy, damp basket down and then lifting it, even heavier after watering and struggling to find the overhead hook on which to hang it is not easy. On the whole I have found that the light-weight wire baskets are the most agreeable to use in any situation. The wire is easily hidden.

Making a hanging basket

Use potting mix, garden soil is not porous enough. Make certain the peat in the mix is well-shredded and evenly distributed otherwise there could be clumps into which water would find it difficult to penetrate.

Plant young herbs. Consideration must be given to both the immediate and long-term effect. Until creeping herbs have crept and begun to hang down gracefully, hang the basket low. The bare under-side of a basket is not the prettiest of sights.

Buying well-grown plants means that a simple basket is quickly and easily made, but if you are prepared to take more time and trouble the results can be more spectacular.

Baskets are best hung on a bracket which keeps them clear of the wall.

Wherever and however you choose to hang them it is important to keep them out of the wind or draughts and in a position which facilitates watering. If you can get away with not taking the basket down to be watered you will need a hose or a long-necked watering-can.

Hanging baskets need watching to see that they stay moist. In hot weather they might need water twice a day.

Test with the finger to see if the top soil feels dry, if it does they need water. It is a good idea to add some soluble fertiliser to their drink every few weeks.

Pinching out growing tips and removing dead flowers will keep the plants growing steadily.

There are so many herbs from which to choose. It is best, I think, not to have too many different sorts in a basket. A bit of this and a bit of that does not make for a tasteful effect.

Catmint, thyme, low-growing rosemary, hyssop, oregano, chamomile are only a few of the herbs which look lovely grown this way. They all like the sun.

If the basket has a shady side, vinca and pennyroyal will be quite happy to grow there.

A quick method

1 Line a basket with sphagnum moss and cover it with black plastic which has been punctured all over to make drainage holes.

2 Half-fill the basket with well-soaked potting mix.

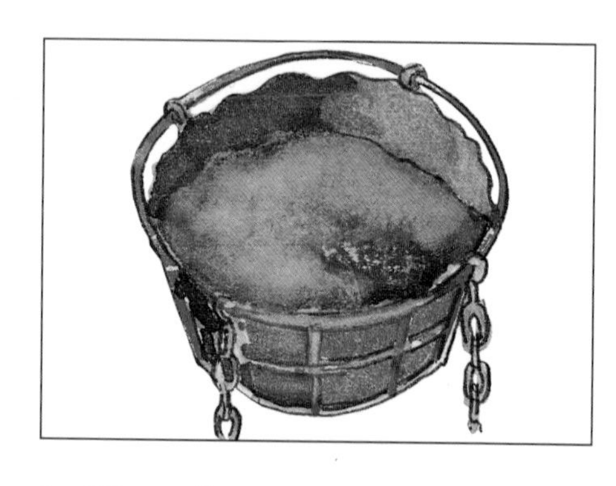

3 Tip well-grown little plants out of their pots, loosen the soil and snuggle each one into the potting mix and firm in. Plant trailing herbs around the outside and medium-sized ones in the centre.

4 Add more potting mix if needed, water gently until the water is draining out of the bottom then hang in the shade for a few days to enable the plants to adjust to their new environment.

Left: *Overhanging and trailing foliage is the key to a pretty hanging basket.*

MAKING A HANGING BASKET

1 Line the basket with sphagnum moss which has been left to soak overnight. Be generous. The moss should be at least 4 cm/2 inches thick and should overlap the top edges of the basket like pastry over a pie-dish. Press the moss well in and through the wire so that most of the wire is concealed.

2 Planting can be tricky. Poke holes in the moss and put the plants head first through them from the inside of the basket. Since they are young and delicate it is important not to damage either leaves or roots. Little plastic bags will help. Pop the plant into the bag head first and before insertion roll the plastic round it gently.

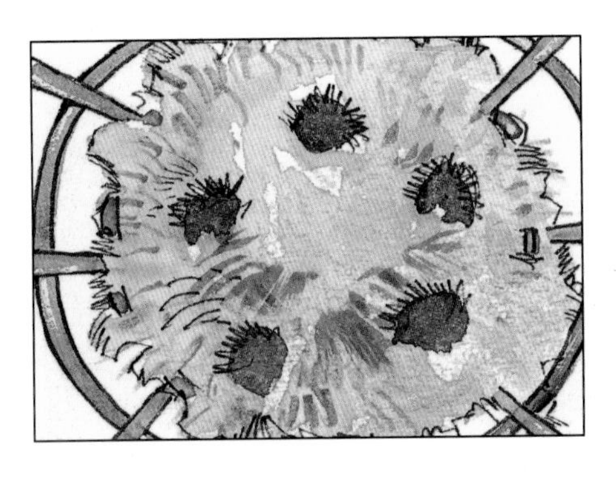

3 Make holes about 7 cm/3 inches apart in the base of the basket. Use judgement as to the size needed to get the plant safely through.

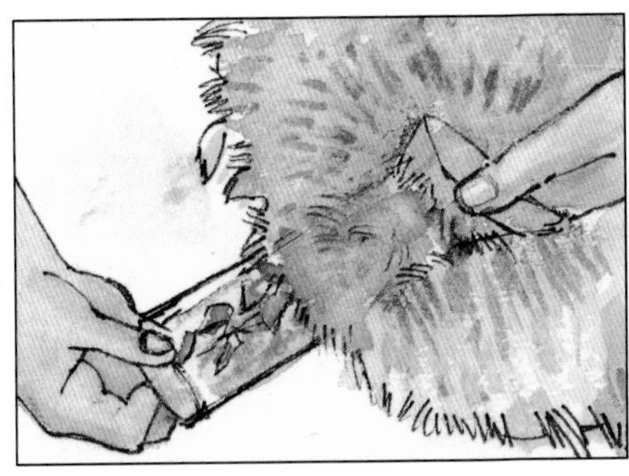

4 Insert the plants one by one head first and remove the bags. Cover the roots carefully with well moistened potting mix.

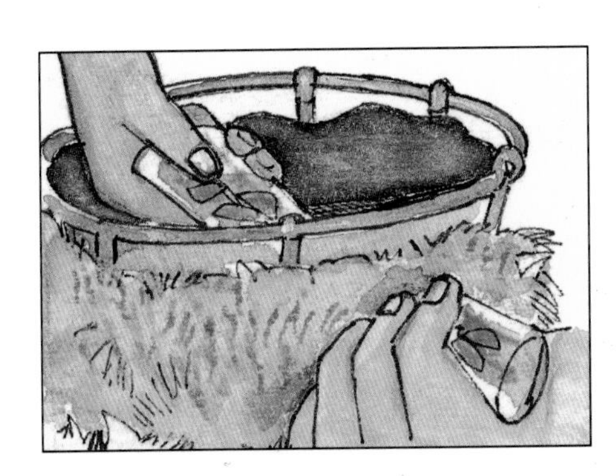

5 Make holes in the moss around the circumference of the basket, repeat the planting process and carefully cover the roots with moistened potting mix and firm them in before filling the basket with more mix.

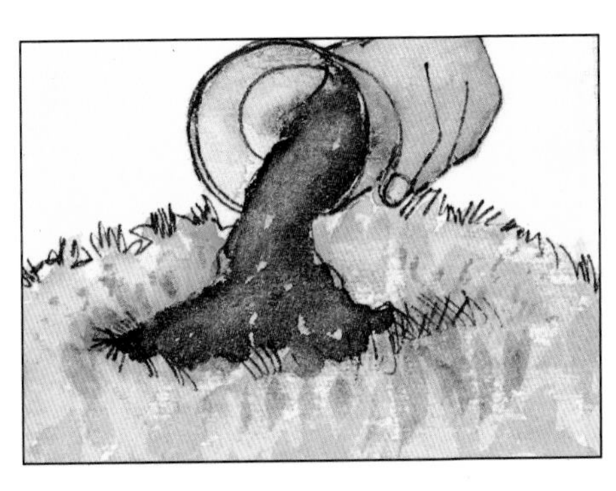

6 Plant the soil at the top of the basket normally. Water very gently until the water drips out of the bottom of the basket then hang it in the shade for a few days until the plants settle in.

HERBS FOR A HANGING BASKET

Select plants which are sympathetic to the shape of the container. Choose plants whose leaves appear to grow in layers or horizontal mounds. Look for herbs which arch gracefully or which trail. Upright plants are not suitable unless they are surrounded by other shapes to soften their appearance.

For a sunny location

- *creeping thymes—caraway-scented thyme , lemon-scented thyme, pine-scented thyme*
- *catmint*
- *ivies*
- *prostrate winter savory*
- *prostrate rosemary*
- *sage*
- *lady's mantle*

For a shady location

- *pennyroyal*
- *variegated mints*
- *ginger mint*
- *periwinkle*

If you have chosen a very big basket a second planting round the circumference may be necessary so make the depth of the potting mix covering the roots of the first planting adequate before making the second planting and filling the basket with mix. Only low-growing and trailing herbs should be used in an arrangement like this. A planting of just one type of herb is surprisingly effective.

HERBS IN WINDOW-BOXES

If you don't have a garden, don't have room for herbs to grow in pots or in hanging baskets, don't despair—many a herb garden has been grown on a window sill.

Low-growing herbs are the most suitable. Parsley, chives, mints, thyme, tarragon, marjoram can be the staples.

Cuttings of larger plants such as lavender, sage and scented geranium will add variety.

Does the position of the box allow drain holes through which water can safely escape? If not you must make provision.

1 Make a box about 30 cm/12 inches deep. Cover the base with a layer of rough material—brick rubble, gravel, clinker, broken pot, then a layer of peat to help retain moisture.

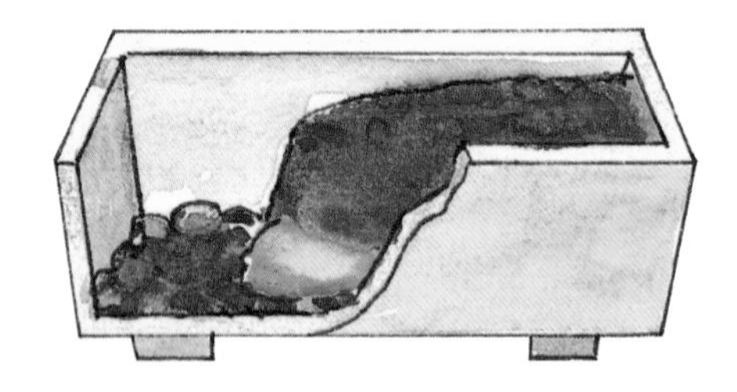

2 Finally add a good potting mix which has been well dampened. This should allow for drainage into the rubble and adequate water retention in the peat.

3 Watering should be slow and careful and not over-done. Test the top soil and water when it feels dry to the touch, and keep the plants growing steadily by pinching out the growing points and removing dead flowers.

ESSENTIAL HERBS FOR WINDOW BOXES

- ***Basil:*** *Prevent flowering for long life; sow again in midsummer for late use.*
- ***Chives:*** *Keep well fertilised and watered.*
- ***Parsley:*** *Sow in spring and again in late summer.*
- ***Thyme:*** *Can be started from either seed or cuttings. Water sparingly.*
- ***Chervil:*** *Sow in spring and again in late summer.*
- ***Marjoram:*** *Grow like thyme.*
- ***Sage:*** *Strike cuttings and trim frequently.*

Salad herbs in pots grow well in semi-shade and can always be at hand near the kitchen door.

Herb Cultivation

Herbs are, on the whole, good-natured plants, happy to grow among flowers and vegetables and with each other. They are pleasantly informal plants, given the chance they will sprawl and spread and wander. Hardship brings out the best in them. Their flavour is less pungent when grown in gentle conditions.

Herbs are on the whole good-natured plants, happy to grow among flowers and vegetables and with each other. There are however, some good "haters" among them. Basil and sage will kill each other if forced to live together—mint and parsley droop if grown in the same bed and every herb but dill complains if planted near fennel.

Herbs love the sun—without it they lose much of their potency and flavour so whatever type of garden is planned the siting of it is very important. The soil does not have to be rich—in fact many of them prefer a poorish one—but it does have to be well-drained for they hate to have their "feet" in a puddle. This is particularly so for plants with tough, narrow leaves like thyme, rosemary and lavender—and to a lesser extent, oregano.

They don't mind a poorish soil and can cope with a certain amount of dryness but most of them like plenty of sun. Many of the small-leaved ones popular for cooking are natives of the Mediterranean area where they are accustomed to struggling for life on stony ground or between rocks under a hot sun with only occasional rain to offer them a drink. Hardship seems to bring out the best in them for their flavour is less pungent when grown in gentler conditions.

The softer and broader the leaf, the richer the soil needed. Basil and parsley enjoy their food.

Before deciding what type of garden you want it is as well to grow acquainted with the scents, colours, needs and properties of the great range of herbs from which to choose.

Colour is always important in a garden and while herbs do not have particularly large flowers they can look striking when massed.

Lavender is among the most versatile and useful herbs. It can be used medicinally, for the pleasure of its fragrance, in body care and cooking.

Friable soil is low in clay but will hold together by virtue of its organic matter.

REQUIREMENTS

Herbs are the least demanding and least difficult plants to grow. By and large all they require is a well-drained, friable soil and sunshine. They do not need fertilisers or manures, they are not demanding about water, they do not need protection against predators and are not prone to disease.

They grow easily from seed, from cuttings and from root division.

They are good-tempered about being moved. Herbs are not sulkers.

GROWING FROM SEED

Seeds can be sown directly into the ground or in boxes.

Since herbs are usually reliable seeders, thinning out will be necessary for the ones sown direct. The seeds sown in boxes have to be potted on. The little plants can grow in their first pot until large enough to plant out or can be transferred to a larger pot if they are to be grown in a portable garden.

There are certain herbs which do not enjoy the root disturbance which is part of transplanting and should be sown direct. These include anise, chervil, coriander, cumin, dill and parsley.

It is wise to consider how many plants of each type are needed. It may not be necessary to go through the time-consuming process of growing seed as one can end up with far too many plants. It is more sensible to buy one or two plants.

When the soil has warmed after winter chill, rake it over to break up any lumps, mark out a shallow drill, and, if you think your soil is not fine enough, dribble some fine sand along the drill before planting the seeds. Cover them lightly with friable soil, water gently and firm the soil.

Thin out or transplant the seedlings when they are 7-10 cm/3-4 inches high and the first pair of true leaves have appeared.

The transplanted seedlings should be kept in the shade and sheltered at night for the first few days to enable them to get over the stress of being moved. If you intend to plant them out, first give them a week or two in the pot and when you replant keep the soil ball around the roots intact.

HERBS WHICH GROW EASILY FROM SEED

angelica, basil, borage, calendula, caraway, catmint, chamomile, chives, fennel, hyssop, lovage, marjoram, marshmallow, mustard, oregano, sage, sweet cicely, thyme, wormwood

SOFTWOOD CUTTINGS

These can be taken from new growth or after the plant has finished flowering.

Choose a healthy stem that is not carrying a flower bud and cut it just below a leaf node 7 cm to 10 cm/3 to 4 inches from the top of the stem. Remove all the lower leaves.

Coarse river sand is the best medium in which to strike cuttings but a light sandy soil with some added peat or a proprietary potting mix will do. The important thing is to ensure good drainage but still have adequate water retention.

Whatever medium you use, water it thoroughly before inserting the cutting.

Using a pencil or chopstick make a hole in the sandy soil deep enough for the cutting to be inserted with one or two leaf-nodes below the soil and only a short stem and the top leaves above it. Now insert the cutting and firm it in. Many cuttings can be fitted into one large pot.

Keep the pot in the shade while the cuttings are developing roots.

It helps to give a light spray when watering the soil.

A very simple way is to insert cuttings in the soil all around the edge of an ordinary-sized pot and water the soil well then enclose the whole pot in a plastic bag large enough and strong enough to stand up away from the leaves. The pot should be kept in a warm place but out of the sun and opened and resealed every two or three days to let air in and prevent mould building up.

The cuttings should root in from five to six weeks.

HARDWOOD CUTTINGS

Hardwood cuttings and semi-hardwood cuttings are taken from shrubby plants in much the same way as softwood ones, but the soft growing point must be pinched out as well as the leaves from the lower part of the stem. The cuttings are taken at the end of the flowering season. If left outdoors in pots during winter they should be given protection.

ROOT CUTTINGS

These are taken from perennial plants with strong roots.

The root is dug up and pieces are cut from it, each one with its own growing point and are planted either in the ground or in a pot. The soil must be kept moist as growth appears.

DIVISION

Many perennial herbs are easily separated and pulled apart to make several plants each with its own roots. This is best done in early spring.

Each separated piece should be carefully settled in its new position and trimmed neatly. It will need careful watering while it is adapting to life on its own and putting out its own new roots.

STRIKING CUTTINGS

1 Choose a healthy stem that is not carrying a flower bud and cut it just below a leaf node 7 cm to 10 cm/3 to 4 inches from the top. Remove all the lower leaves.

2 Coarse river sand is the best medium but a light sandy soil with some added peat or a proprietary potting mix will do. Water thoroughly.

3 Make a hole deep enough for the cutting to be inserted with one or two leaf-nodes below the soil and only a short stem and the top leaves above it.

HERB GROWING HABITS

Tall Herbs
angelica, bay, coriander, dill, fennel, golden rod, lovage, rosemary

Medium-sized herbs
borage, bergamot, lemongrass, sage, tarragon

Low-growing herbs
basil, catmint, lemon balm, marjoram, mint, oregano, parsley, thyme

Spreading growth
catmint, chamomile, lemon balm

Annual herbs
basil, borage, coriander

Biennial herbs
angelica

Perennial herbs
balm, bergamot, chamomile, golden rod, lovage, mint, parsley, rosemary, sage

Herbs for hedges
box, hyssop, lavender, marjoram, rosemary, sage, santolina, southernwood, wormwood

Herbs for ground cover
ajuga, chamomile, golden rod marjoram, lady's bedstraw, pennyroyal, prostrate rosemary, thyme, violet, woodruff

Herbs for shade
aconite, ajuga, angelica, balm, betony, chervil, comfrey, germander, golden marjoram, lovage, mint, parsley, rosemary, tarragon, woodruff, wormwood

Herbs which need moisture
angelica, bergamot, lovage, mint, pennyroyal

Herbs for a dry soil
agrimony, arnica, borage, burnet, chamomile, chicory, fennel, lavender, rosemary, sage, santolina, thyme, yarrow

Angelica archangelica, named after the archangel, was used in medieval times as a sentinel to protect lambs from the curse of a witch.

LAYERING

This is a simple process in which a stem, still attached to a plant, is stretched out along the ground, underside down, and pegged into position. A very little earth can cover it. It will slowly develop roots of its own from points along the stem and, once established, the plant can be severed from its parent and transplanted to start a life of its own.

LAYERING

1 Select a flexible branch low down on the plant, remove some of the leaves where it touches the soil. Cut a notch to start the new rooting system.

2 Dig out a shallow depression in the soil and hold the prepared section of the branch in place with a wire loop or a clothes peg.

3 Cover the mounded section of the layered branch and wire loop with top soil, and gently firm. Only water the layered area to hasten growth.

HERBS TO REPEL INSECTS

Many herbs give off a scent which insects do not like. You can use a barrier of herbs to protect plants against insects Plant so that the scent is strong. and will mask the scent of the herb which is attracting the pest.

To keep aphids away: horseradish, tansy, thyme and yarrow

To repel the cabbage butterfly: basil, caraway, chives, coriander, nasturtium and tansy

To repel the carrot fly: coriander, mint, rosemary, sage and tansy

To control caterpillars: marjoram

To control cutworms: tansy

To control eelworms: calendula

To repel mosquitoes: Mosquitoes don't like basil, tansy and southernwood so a pot on the windowsill or near outside doors will help to keep them out of the house.

HERBS WHICH ATTRACT BIRDS AND BUTTERFLIES

basil, bergamot, borage, catmint, lavender, lemon balm, marjoram, mint, rosemary, sage, thyme, yarrow

ATTRACTING BENEFICIAL INSECTS

Not all insects are enemies; there are many which help the gardener and should be encouraged.

Ladybirds, for example, eat aphids, scale insects, mealy bugs, leaf-hoppers, white flies, mites and the beetle of both the potato and tomato.

Hoverflies, which are like silent little wasps, eat aphids and their larvae, mealy bugs and grasshoppers.

Lacewings are small insects with gauzy wings and golden eyes. They eat aphids, caterpillars, thrips, scale insects and mealy bugs.

Centipedes and millipedes do not attack plants that are growing well—they like dead or dying ones.

One of the ways to assist beneficial insects is to grow herbs with small flowers. Many beneficial insects, including lacewings, need to eat pollen and nectar in order to complete their life cycle; many other insects can use pollen and nectar as a temporary food supply in the absence of pests. Dill, sage, fennel, thyme, Roman chamomile, yarrow, and a number of other herbs are good choices.

GOOD HERB COMPANIONS

Basil: apricots, asparagus, grapes, parsley and tomatoes

Borage: strawberries

Calendula: beans, lettuce, potatoes, roses, tomatoes

Chamomile: cabbage and mint

It is good to have around anywhere because it has the ability to encourage nearby plants to increase their essential oil and so taste and smell more strongly

Chives: apples, carrots, cucumber, parsley and tomatoes

Chervil: dill, coriander

Coriander: cabbage and carrots

Dill: cabbage, celery, carrots and tomatoes

Foxgloves: tomatoes, potatoes, apples

Horseradish: apples, apricots and potatoes

Hyssop: cabbage and grapes

Garlic: apples, parsnips, peaches, roses

Lavender: silver beet

Left: Grow insect repellent herbs in a window box.

Marigolds: lettuce, potatoes, tomatoes, roses

Marjoram: cucumbers

Mint: cabbages

Nasturtiums: apples, cabbages, cauliflowers, broccoli, brussels sprouts, kohlrabi, turnips, courgettes, carrots, cucumber, grapes and radishes

Oregano: cabbages, cucumbers

Parsley: asparagus, roses, chives, tomatoes

Rosemary: cabbages, carrots

Sage: cabbages, carrots, roses

Savory: beans, onions

Southernwood: apricots, roses

Tansy: apples, apricots, cabbages, cauliflowers, broccoli, brussels sprouts, beans, grapes, peaches, raspberries, roses

Thyme: beans, cabbages, cauliflowers

Parsley: mint, broccoli, brussels sprouts

BAD COMPANIONS

Caraway: parsnips

Chives: beans, beet, onions

Coriander: fennel

Dill: strawberries

Fennel: coriander, beans, tomatoes, kohlrabi, wormwood

Garlic: peas, beans, cabbages, strawberries

Hyssop: radishes

Mint: parsley

Rosemary: potatoes, tomatoes

Rue: basil, sage

Sage: basil, rue, wormwood

Wormwood: all other plants

Top: *Marigolds and borage protecting young lettuce are colourful and edible in their own right.*

Harvesting Herbs

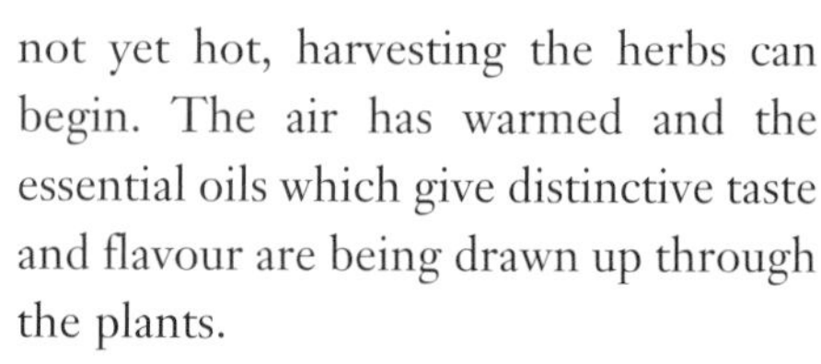

Capture and preserve the wonderful summertime aroma and flavour of your favourite herbs by picking them at their best and leaving them to dry. You can use dried herbs for cooking, in bath-time preparations, fragrant sachets and potpourri mixtures.

Choosing which herbs to dry and deciding how much of each one is needed is very much a personal choice. Happy the gardener with great beds of parsley and basil so that fresh ones are available for a longish time and enough of them can be kept in the freezer to last until the next crop. To dry them is to ask for disappointment.

GATHERING HERBS

When the herbs are in full leaf and the flowers have formed but are not yet open, it is time to gather together a flat-bottomed basket and a pair of neat, sharp garden scissors and to scan the sky. On a bright morning, when there is no trace of mugginess in the air, when the morning dew has dried but the sun is not yet hot, harvesting the herbs can begin. The air has warmed and the essential oils which give distinctive taste and flavour are being drawn up through the plants.

Gathering herbs must be a very gentle process. Leaves, stems and flowers bruise easily and so must be handled lightly.

With one hand facing upward, spread apart the forefinger and second finger and slide them round the stem to be snipped. Allow the leaves or flower to rest gently on the fingers. Make the snip and transfer the cut stem to the basket, laying it down gently.

Work quickly—herbs begin to lose their vital properties the minute the stem is cut. Do not pick more than can be prepared for drying in a very short time. When one batch is drying there can be a sortie into the garden to pick another one.

DRYING HERBS

The aim is to dry the herbs keeping as much of their colour and flavour as possible so the sooner the drying can begin the better. Loss of moisture must be

One of the pleasures of working with herbs is gathering them. This must be done carefully to avoid bruising. They must be handled lightly.

Left: *Herbs dry best out of the sun and with open ventilation.*
Below: *Herbs dried in a flower press are delightful on letters or greeting cards.*

gradual and steady—a quick frizzle will result in a pile of brown dust. A dried leaf should still be green, but brittle, and easily stripped, whole, from the stem. If it crumbles when touched it has been overdone. Two to three days to a week or more, depending on the size and thickness of the material being dried is usual.

Try not to wash herbs before use.

A dry, warm, airy spot, away from the light is ideal for drying herbs.

A shed with an open, shuttered door—a room with open shuttered windows—a space under the house—but NOT a garage. There will be petrol fumes around.

And not the kitchen. Steam from the cooking will do them no good at all.

Bunches of herbs hung to dry should be small, a dozen stems at most, and one type of herb only to each bunch. Secure the bunch with string or an elastic band. String is better. Tie the stems safely but not too tightly—air must be able to flow through the bunches or mould will take hold—and make a loop. Hang the loop with the herbs head downwards from a hook where air can flow all round them—not against a wall.

If you have to wash herbs before drying them, let them hang, head down until as much water as possible has drained away, then separate them into small bunches. Tie each one separately and put the head downwards into a brown paper bag, large enough to give air space all around the heads and tie the bag in place. Hang in a warm, dry place until the contents of the bag rustle. You will probably have to finish the drying in a slow oven.

If you are going in for drying in a big way, search around for an old-fashioned clothes rack—the kind that used to hang in the kitchen and could be let down and drawn up. It will take dozens of bunches at a time.

If you were to store it under the house, for instance, it would be wise to tie an open-bottomed paper bag round each bunch as protection against dust.

DRYING HERBS ON THE FLAT

A small amount of herbs spread out between two sheets of kitchen paper on an oven or cake rack will dry quite well.

Fly screens, large or small, with butter muslin stretched tightly across them, laid down horizontally and raised on bricks to allow air to circulate above and below, make ideal drying platforms for larger amounts.

An old bunk bed stripped of mattresses works in the same way.

The leaves and flowers are laid out in a single layer on the muslin, covered by another piece of muslin, and left for a week or longer to dry. Do not be impatient—flower heads and thick leaves carry quite an amount of moisture.

You can dry herbs in this way outdoors only if absolutely certain of the weather—an unexpected shower or sudden wind gust would mean ruin.

A large amount of leaves and flowers placed on a tray between two sheets of absorbent paper would have to be turned every day to ensure they dried evenly so it is worth the initial trouble of setting up the fly screens.

DRYING SEEDS

Tie up the herbs as described but encase the heads in a paperbag before hanging. This will collect seeds which dry and fall.

DRYING QUICKLY

If you want drying to be completed in hours, not days, try the oven method.

Spread out the herbs in a single layer on a sheet of strong paper or a paper-covered oven sheet and place in an oven turned to its lowest setting.

Leave the door slightly open. You will probably have to jam it to keep it steady. Inspect herbs after an hour. They should still be green but brittle.

DRYING ROOTS

Roots should be scrubbed, peeled, cut into small sections and dried in an oven heated to about 50°C /120°F. They need to be turned every now and then. They are done when they snap.

DRYING IN THE MICROWAVE OVEN

Instructions are usually given in the booklet which comes with the oven.

By and large the thing to remember is that herbs contain volatile oils which could combust if heat becomes too high.

Drying a cupful of herbs at a time is the best way to start.

Spread the clean dry herbs between two sheets of kitchen paper and microwave on High for one minute.

Check to see if any have dried. If they have remove them, move the remainder around and heat for another 20 seconds. Continue heating and removing the dried ones until all are dry.

HERBS THAT DO NOT DRY WELL

Basil, balm, coriander, chives, mint, parsley and tarragon should be stored frozen.

Tuck sprigs or leaves into small plastic bags, expel the air and roll up to seal. A number of these small bags can be kept inside a large, labelled bag in the freezer to be used as needed. It is not necessary to chop the herbs before freezing.

When they defrost they will be too limp to use in salads or as garnishes but they are as good as fresh ones for cooked dishes.

Herbs that are to be used medicinally should not be frozen. Use them dried.

DESICCANT DRYING

Lovely bouquets can be made from flowers and foliage which have been dried this way. Silica gel is sold especially for the purpose or you can use builder's sand, or powdered borax, or a mixture of borax and cornflour. A shoebox makes a good container.

Prepare each flower by cutting off the stem and replacing it with a length of florist's wire pushed through the centre of the head. Attach sprigs and leaves to the wire to make a pretty floral arrangement. Don't be too ambitious to start with. Keep things small.

Top: *Herbs hanging to dry.*

Opposite *Oil takes on the flavour of fresh herbs and makes a wonderful addition to salads and dressings.*

Place a layer of desiccant in the box. Shake desiccant through the flower and leaves, making sure it goes between every one, then lay the 'piece' down flat. There may be room for more than one—they must not touch each other. Cover with enough desiccant to ensure that a new layer of flowers will not touch the ones already laid down and repeat the procedure until the box is almost full. Top it off with desiccant, put on the lid and store the box in a warm, dry place.

Inspect after about a week. The flowers and leaves are not ready until they are crisp.

When completely dry, carefully shake away all the desiccant.

If you are dexterous the use of more florist's wire and green crepe paper could further enhance the flowers.

PRESERVING WITH GLYCERINE

Large stems of lavender, rosemary, bay, eucalyptus, sorrel, etc can be steeped in a mixture of glycerine and water to preserve them.

Hammer the bottom of the stems and place the stems in a large jug containing two parts of hot water to one of glycerine—enough to cover about the bottom 5 cm/2 inches of stem. Stand the jug in a warm, light place and inspect after a day or so. Add more glycerine and water to keep the stems covered to the required depth for the next three weeks. Cut away the smashed and sticky ends, wipe any excess oil from the leaves and use as decoration.

STORING HERBS

Herbs in storage need to be protected against light, damp and attack by insects.

Collect brown or green glass jars. Coloured jars are the most effective containers for storing herbs.

Keep your herbs in the large jars or "mother" jars in a dark cupboard and use the small jars in a rack near the cooking area, refilling from the "mother" jar as required.

Air in the jar takes away their keeping qualities so as the quantity of herbs in the large jars falls.fill the space with cotton wool. Both jars should be labelled with the name and date of storage. It is dangerous to try to rely on memory—herbs look alike when they are dried, and after a year are past their best.

STORING HERBS IN SALT

This is another method for preserving herbs that do not dry well.

Common salt or sea salt, not table salt, should be used.

In a lidded container put down a thick layer of salt. Place a layer of herbs, half the depth of the salt, on top and cover by a layer of salt of the same depth. Continue layering, finishing with a final layer of salt.

When herbs are needed, take them out, shake off the salt and use normally.

The salt will take on the flavour of the herbs and can be used in cooking.

STORING HERBS IN OIL

Use best quality olive oil. The fresh, dry herb leaves are just covered with oil in a jar, sealed and kept in a dark place. Take a few out for use in cooking as needed.

The oil takes on the flavour of the herbs and can be used in salad dressing or cooking.

WILD ROSE
Christophoriana

Herbal Fragrance

The scent of herbs is sweet, light and lingering; it lies gently on the air, delicate and wholesome, never too obtrusive. It can make a time and a place stay in the memory for a lifetime. There are many lovely ways in which we can bring that elusive fragrance into our homes.

HERB PILLOWS

When pillows were made of straw, sweet-smelling herbs were added so as to reduce odours and repel germs. We do not have those problems today but a little herb sachet tucked inside a pillow-case will give pleasure for its scent and even act as an inducement to easy sleep. The choice among sweetly scented herbs is wide. We each have our own favourites and can make mixes to please our own taste.

Suggested Mixtures:

- rose petals and lavender
- rosemary, mignonette, rose petals
- verbena, marjoram, lavender
- woodruff, mint, chamomile
- scented geranium, rose petals
- peppermint, chamomile, woodruff
- agrimony, woodruff, hops
- mint, balm, verbena, rose petals
- rose petals, lemon verbena, rosemary, lavender

Pillow mixtures for sleepless nights

A pillow stuffed with hops can be of real help to insomniacs.

If you don't like the beery smell, add some dried rosemary, lavender or verbena to disguise it.

OR try this mix:

4 cups (1 litre) hops
2 tbsp dried lemon verbena leaves
2 tbsp dried, grated orange peel
2 tbsp dried orris root
3 drops essential orange-blossom oil

Below: *Herb pillows lend themselves to cross-stitch, embroidery, ribbon and lace. Dried aromatic herbs look a picture in a pretty cane basket. There is a wide choice of fragrant herbs which will delicately scent the air.*

OR

2 cups (500 ml) each dried rose petals, and dried mint leaves
1 tbsp ground cloves

When making the mix you can, if you wish, add a little orris powder to help fix the scent, some ground spice and a little pot-pourri. The scent will last for a year or more. When it needs enlivening add a few drops of your favourite essential oil— but be sparing—a few drops go a long way.

A complaint sometimes made is that the dried herbs in a pillow crackle disturbingly when the head is moved. If rustling or crackling is likely to irritate you, sprinkle the herbs with water which contains a little glycerine before you make the pillow or sachet.

If you have enough ingredients you can stuff a full-sized pillow or cushion, but if you do not, make some little cheesecloth or muslin bags to contain the mix, give them some pretty covers which can be removed for washing, and tuck them inside the pillow-case or cushion. The little bags can also be put among linen and in the undies drawer, or they could be hung from a length of ribbon to scent the wardrobe.

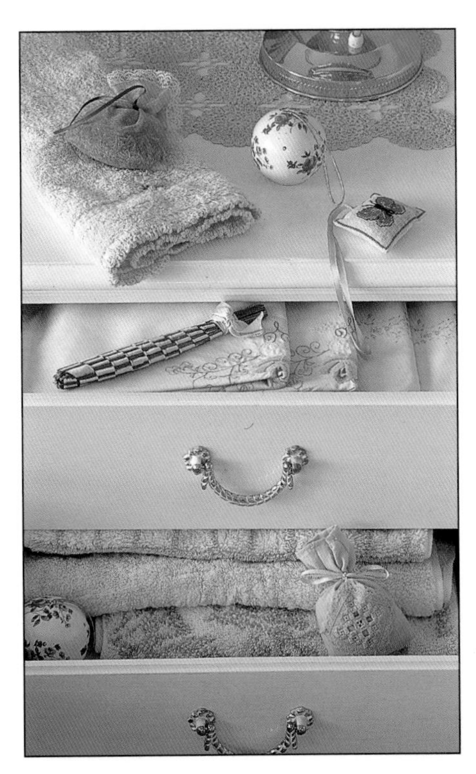

Above: *Scented sachets can be made in a variety of styles and sizes.*
Below left: *There is nothing quite so fresh and fragrant as handkerchiefs and underwear taken scented from a drawer.*

SACHETS

Repelling moths
The scent is strong and more pleasant than the traditional mothball.

125 ml/½ cup each dried lavender and rosemary
1 tbsp dried southernwood leaves

OR
250 ml/1 cup dried mint leaves
63 ml/¼ cup each dried southernwood, tansy and lavender
1 tbsp powdered cloves

Mix the ingredients together and sew them into small muslin bags. These can be hung in wardrobes or put among woollies in summer storage. Fit one around a padded coat hanger before putting on the ornamental coating. Small sachets of these mixtures tucked among books will stop them developing a musty smell and will also keep insects away.

The advised proportions when using spices and powdered citrus is 15 ml/ 1 tablespoon to 50 g/2 oz dried herbs.

SCENTING LINEN, TOWELS AND DRAWERS

Fresh and spicy
Mix dried lavender, lemon verbena, peppermint and rosemary in any proportion you choose, and add a touch of dried cloves and cinnamon.

Coat lightly in orris root powder before adding a few drops each of lavender, lemon verbena and peppermint oil.

Mix, very gently, and add the oil a drop at a time, sniffing as you go and remembering that you can add more if needed but you can't take any out.

Soft and sweet
Mix dried rose petals, dried marjoram, lavender and some finely crushed dried orange peel lightly covered in orris root powder with the addition of a few drops of rose oil and lavender oil—more rose than lavender. Mix as for "Fresh and spicy".

SWEET HERBAL RINSES

My grandmother used to spread her sheets over the lavender hedge to dry and the memory of lifting them and folding them and holding them to the face to inhale their soft fragrance remains.

The simplest way I have found of getting the same effect is to boil up handfuls of fresh lavender flowers in water to give about a 5 cm/2 inch cover and then to hold it on a lively simmer for 10 minutes or so. Use the strained liquid in the final rinse cycle of the washing machine.

If you save some you can sprinkle it over sheets and garments before ironing.

Other herbs can be used—eau-de-cologne, mint, bay leaves, rosemary, hyssop, marjoram, balm.

POMANDERS

1 thin-skinned orange
50 g/2 oz whole cloves
2 tbsp orris root powder
2 tsp ground cinnamon

1 The whole orange is covered with cloves but, since it is to be hung up, we have to leave a narrow space all round the circumference so that ribbon can be tied on. Stud the orange with the cloves, leaving a space between each one to allow for shrinkage. You may have to pierce the skin with a darning needle to get the dried cloves firmly embedded.
2 When the orange is completely covered, press the mixed spices all over the fruit as evenly as possible and then do the same with the orris root powder. This will fix the fragrance.
3 Put the orange in a paper bag and leave it in a dark, dry place where air is circulating for 3 weeks to a month. By then it should be thoroughly dry.
4 Fit the ribbon into the groove left for it, tie, make a loop and hang in the wardrobe.

If after a few years the scent fades, paint it over with some essential oil

Top: *Finished fragranced pomanders.*
Middle: *Draw a pattern on the orange using a marking pen or indelible pencil. Leave a space around the circumference for the ribbon.*
Left: *Make holes in the skin with a darning needle and firmly imbed the cloves.*

mixed with a touch of clove oil to restore the pungency.

SCENTING ROOMS

An old country ploy to keep a room sweetly scented was to rub the wooden furniture with the crushed leaves of balm, verbena, marjoram, mint or any strong and sweetly scented flower—a precursor of our room fresheners.

If you run out of bought incense sticks try using lavender stalks stripped of their flowers instead.

If desperate to hide an unpleasant smell quickly, heat some sprigs of rosemary or thyme, or some mixed spice or some whole or powdered cloves in an old, heavy frying pan and when it is smoking gently take it to where the smell is most noticeable and stay there for a few minutes before carrying the pan around the house just to make sure.

You can use other herbs but make sure they have a clean, sharp scent—the sweet scents don't work as well.

HERBAL INCENSE

Fragrant smoke has risen to the heavens as long as man has prayed to his gods—sweet herbs were burned as offerings to Ra, the Egyptian sun-god, the light of the world. When Greeks made their altar sacrifices incense was also burned to make the offering more pleasing to the deity; temples and palaces were sweetened and purified by burning aromatic herbs and in later years censors containing incense were swung in churches and cathedrals as Catholics celebrated High Mass and other religious ceremonies and they are still in use today.

The North American Indians not only used smoke to send signals to each other but burned sweet herbs to purify themselves and their environment as they sent up prayers to the Great Spirit and sought communication with the unseen power that guides us all.

Today we burn incense in our homes, not so much with religion in mind as the pleasure given and the atmosphere created by the fragrant smoke. The scent is clean—the air seems purer.

MAKING INCENSE

The simplest method of all is to pour some rosewater over powdered cloves and mix it in. After a few days the scent will have matured.

If you have a room which has been closed up and smells musty—heat an old iron pan, sprinkle a little of the powder over it, put it in the room and close the door. In the old days housewives used a special perfuming pan. I have searched antique shops in vain but there must be some to be found somewhere.

LOOSE INCENSE

Loose incense which is thrown on burning charcoal or is made into briquettes is the least complicated to make.

75 g/3 oz powdered frankincense
50 g/2 oz powdered orris root
25 g/l oz powdered cloves
25 g/l oz sandalwood shavings
A few drops of your favourite essential oil

The atmosphere and mood can be varied by softly burning fragrant herbal incense.

Mix all the dry ingredients together, sprinkle with the oil and store in a cool dark place for 8 to 10 weeks for the perfume to mature.

It can be used, a teaspoonful at a time, in an incense dish, or thrown over a smouldering fire or some burning charcoal.

DOUGH INCENSE

Dough incense is rather different. For making this you will need a blender, bowls and a wooden spoon.

- **sweet scented dried herbs or spices**
- **half the amount of the above of scented wood-bark shavings**
- **tragacanth powder**
- **potassium nitrate (saltpeter)**
- **water**
- **food colouring (optional)**

The amount of ingredients can vary.

1 Mix the dried herbs and spices with the dried scented barks which you have reduced to powder in the blender.
2 Mix the potassium nitrate with a little water. Add tragacanth powder and mix to a smooth paste, adding more water if needed.
3 Add dried herbs and continue mixing adding water and tragacanth powder as needed until you have a smooth paste which can be formed into firm shapes.

Tragacanth powder

Tragacanth is a mucilaginous plant substance used for giving firmness to pills and capsules. It is available at chemist shops. So is potassium nitrate.

If you are afraid the scent is not going to be strong enough, add a very few drops of your favourite essential oil.

If you wish, add a little food colouring as you mix.

The paste can be rolled onto bamboo chopsticks, leaving a portion of the lower end bare so that it can be inserted into an incense stick holder—or shaped into cylinders, cones or coils.

The shapes should be left to dry slowly in a warm, airy place.
When thoroughly dry store them in an airtight tin.

It can be seen how easily one can make one's own favourite mixtures.

LOVERS' INCENSE

125 ml/1/2 cup each powdered lavender and rosemary flowers
60 ml/1/4 cup powdered rose petals
500 ml/2 cups sandalwood bark powder
500 ml/2 cups water
1 tsp potassium nitrate
Tragacanth powder to mix

MAKING SCENTED CANDLES

The fragrance of a scented candle is light—much more subtle than that of an incense stick—the soft glow and the drifting perfume make magic on a quiet evening.

You will need

- left-over pieces of candle or some cheap white ones
- some thin string or wicking
- some skewers or chopsticks
- Some muslin sachets of your favourite scented herb, to which you have attached a length of strong cotton. This helps you remove the sachets from the hot wax.

The soft glow and drifting perfume of ornamental candles create charm and warmth in a room.

1 Place the sachets in an old saucepan with the cotton trailing over the edge and assemble your moulds. This is where ingenuity comes in.

Each mould must have a hole in the centre of its base for the wick to be fitted. You will be very lucky if you find anything which will give you a tall, straight or tapering candle but there are many different sizes of waxed food cartons which will do.

2 Coat the inside of each mould with vegetable oil so that the finished candle will slip out easily.

3 Melt your candles in the top of a double saucepan or a jug in the microwave oven. When melted but not too hot, carefully remove any bits of wick.

4 Reheat the wax.

5 While it is heating, tie a piece of string or wick to as many skewers or chopsticks as you have moulds, centring the string on the skewer.

6 Feed the string through the hole on the bottom of the moulds as you lay the skewers or chopsticks across the top of the mould. Pull the string down so that it hangs, taut and vertical.

7 When the wax is hot but not boiling pour it into the saucepan containing the sachets. The heat must be high enough to extract the herb juices that carry the fragrance.

8 Let the wax cool slightly and sniff it. If you don't think the fragrance is strong enough, add a very few drops of the appropriate essential oil. Remove the muslin sachets by the strong cotton.

9 Pour the wax into the moulds making sure that the wick stays in the centre. Leave until cold and hard. Cut the wick and remove the skewer. Remove the candle from the mould. The advantage of using cartons is that they can be peeled away if the candle is stubborn about leaving the mould.

SCENTED WRITING PAPER

Enclose muslin sachets of your favourite dried herb in a new box of writing paper.

SCENTED INK

1 Boil up about 25 g/l oz dried, strongly scented herbs in half a cup of water.

2 Cover and keep simmering for about three quarters of an hour. Watch out or it will boil dry. When there is about 15 ml/4 teaspoonsful of liquid left, strain well, leave to cool, then add to a small bottle of ink.

HERB SCENTED FURNITURE CREAM

115 g/4 oz beeswax
570 ml/20 fl oz turpentine
15 g/½ oz grated soap
350 ml/12 fl oz herbal infusion

1 Dissolve the grated beeswax in the turpentine slowly and carefully over hot water or in the microwave oven—NOT over direct heat. Leave to cool.

2 Make a very strong infusion of your chosen sweet herb (lavender, rosemary, lemon verbena, marjoram etc), boil it up with the grated soap until the soap has melted. Leave to cool.

3 Blend the two mixtures and stir well to produce a smooth cream. Sniff. If the perfume is not strong enough add a drop or so of your chosen essential oil and stir again.

FRAGRANT DISINFECTANTS

Simmer a quantity of rosemary, thyme, bergamot or sage in water just to cover for half an hour. Strain. Use to clean sinks, toilets etc.

PADDED COAT HANGERS

Bought padded coat hangers are often elaborate and frilled—a very simple but pretty one is made by stuffing a long thin tube of muslin with scented herbs and winding it evenly round a coat hanger. This takes care. Smooth and fit into shape and then carefully wind a long strip of pretty material over it so it is completely hidden.

Fasten off neatly. Bind the hook of the hanger with ribbon of a contrasting colour.

HAPPINESS IS A CATMINT BALL

Cats love catmint. The dried leaves and flowers tied up in material make a ball which, pounced on, rolled on, snuggled against, will give off the scent which enchants them. You can, if willing and dexterous enough, make a catmint mouse, complete with tail. The shape is very simple and a little cushion filling added to the catmint will give it a firm shape.

Top: *Catmint balls.*
Right: *Padded coat hangers.*
Below: *Creating your own scented writing paper and scented ink gives your stationery a personal touch.*

SCENTED PIN CUSHIONS

1 Mix some sweet scented, dried herbs with some cushion filling to give body, and roll them up in pretty material to make a sausage.

2 Fasten each end with a tight bow of ribbon and hang in a strategic spot above the sewing table. As pins are stuck in or pulled out a tiny drift of fragrance is released.

Above: *Scented pin cushions.*

Below: *Lavender with its appealing fragrance, is a versatile herb for use in a variety of projects.*

LAVENDER

Most gardeners try to have one lavender bush in their patch but blessed are the ones who have them aplenty.

One of the loveliest sights in a garden is that of butterflies hovering over a lavender hedge, thick with soft, grey-green leaves and shapely spikes of lavender flowers. To stand and take in a deep breath of their clean, sweet fragrance is one of the great garden pleasures.

Plant lavender as lavishly as you can. One bush will give many cuttings and low-growing branches can be layered. The new growth will need attention to its water needs in the initial stages but, once established, lavender looks after itself very well.

Lavender is the background plant par excellence. Its soft colours set off the stronger ones of geraniums, roses, red salvias, blue salvias, pink verbena, petunias, zinnias, cosmos etc. A low-growing hedge of English lavender can wind among the flowers, enhancing the tapestry of colour. Try growing lavender in a bed of old roses just for the blending of perfume alone. The colour contrast is an added bonus.

When one says "lavender" most people think of the English one—French and Italian lavender flowers do not have the same intense fragrance and do not look quite the same, but the bushes have their individual attraction and the difference in the colour of leaves and flowers and the different size and growth-shape make for a very pleasant contrast when they are all grown together.

An abundance of lavender is needed in the garden. We need it to bring fragrance into our homes in so many ways—in pot-pourri, scented pillows and sachets, bouquets, wreaths, cosmetic oils etc. No wonder it has been a mainstay of traditional gardens for so long.

There are over thirty different varieties of lavender—there is a world to explore. There are lavenders with pink, flowers, white flowers, deep purple ones as well as the one which has given its name to a colour.

They all carry the well-loved perfume—they all have an abiding charm.

POTPOURRI

It comes as a surprise to find that "potpourri", a word so evocative of gentle fragrance, actually means "rotted pot". The word is derived from the French verb "pourir" which means "to grow rotten". The name came about by reason of the method once used to retain the fragrance of flowers and herbs.

Roses and lavender flowers have always been popular as the base of a potpourri because they can keep their perfume for a long time without the aid of a fixative, but today though the scent of lavender is as strong as it ever was, how often do we find gardens drenched with the scent of great, pink cabbage roses or many-petalled damask roses as they were in earlier times? To get a real rose scent today you have to search—the ones with the strongest perfume seem to be the single, dark red roses. If all else fails use essential oils.

Roſa Damaſcena flore
pleno

COLLECTING AND DRYING FLOWERS AND LEAVES

No matter how sweetly scented they may be, do not be seduced by white flowers—they can look very dingy when dried.

You can dry violets, roses, lavender, rosemary, marigolds, port-wine magnolia flowers, carnations, mints, marjoram, balm, verbena, chamomile, costmary, woodruff, bergamot, nastutiums, scented leaved geraniums and, for their blue colour, cornflowers, forget-me-nots and plumbago flowers work well. Much of the pleasure of making potpourri is the quiet time spent in the garden making choice.

When you have decided which ones you want to dry, collect a number of large, screw-topped jars-one for each type plus an extra one and keep them on one side.

Drying

1 Choose somewhere quiet and dry—a seldom-used bedroom, the back of a garden shed. You will need a large piece of muslin and an old chair. Cut the muslin to the size made by the four upturned legs. Tie each corner of the muslin to a leg, this will make a tray on which the herbs can be laid. Air will be able to flow above and beneath the fabric.

2 In the mornings when the sun has dried the dew but has not yet become hot, pick your flowers and leaves and spread them out on the muslin, each different variety in its own spot. Leave them to become dry and lightly crisp, then store each one in a labelled, screw-topped jar.

Continue doing this until you feel you have enough material.

Discard anything which has become brown–the leaves should have retained their green, the flowers, their colour.

THE MOIST METHOD

The "moist method" is not popular today largely, one imagines, because the result, though very fragrant, has no eye-appeal at all, whereas the "dry" method smells nice and looks good.

You will need

- a large pot
- plenty of rock salt—NOT a bought packet of salt

sea salt can also be used

- In the morning, when the sun has dried the dew, take a wander through the garden and pick some scented leaves and flowers. You only need enough for a single layer over the base of the pot.

1 Spread a single layer of scented leaves and flowers over the base of the pot. Leave them to wilt for two days.

2 Cover with a thin layer of crumbled rock salt and press gently.

3 Repeat the process over a period of time until the pot is full or your harvest is over. As each layer is added keep it weighed down. Some old-fashioned shop weights on a big meat dish or plate will be fine.

4 A dark sludgy liquid will collect at the bottom of the pot. Stir it through the mixture every now and then so that as much as possible is absorbed and an evenly damp, sweet-smelling "cake" is produced. Leave for a week or two for the "cake" to absorb and retain the fragrances of flower and leaf.

5 Break up the "cake" and put the pieces in a jar with a perforated top to allow the fragrance to escape.

Choose a pretty jar and keep the "cake" well out of sight.

When you pass the jar, if you open it and give it shake, its perfume will drift around the room.

POTPOURRI DELUXE

For a potpourri that has a very long-lasting fragrance a little more time and trouble is needed.

1 Break up the "cake" and mix it with some spices, orris root and lemon or orange peel which you have dried and reduced to a powder. These are fixatives.
2 Add a slurp of brandy as preservative. Up to half a cup if you can spare it.
3 Mix everything well, put back in the pot and leave for six months, covered and weighed down. The scent of the finished product will make up for its looks.

Above: *A potpourri selection of colourful dried flowers ready for scenting.*
Opposite: *Making a potpourri by the "moist" method.*

THE DRY METHOD

The colours of the flowers and leaves are part of the pleasure the mixture gives.

This method is for those with a serious interest—if it is all too much for you there are short cuts.

1 In a jar, blend the flowers and leaves you have collected and dried. Sniff as you go to see how the scent pleases you and distribute the coloured flowers evenly through the mixture. When you have it right add some orris root as a fixative—not much, just enough to make an even snow on the leaves and petals. Carefully powdered, pithless dried citrus peel can be added too but be careful it does not take over the scent. A little powdered gum benzoin (obtainable, as is orris root, from a chemist shop) will ensure the scent holds.
2 Divide the material into equal portions and add some spice and a few drops of essential flower or leaf oil to each one.

You can be as varied as you like. Nutmeg, cloves, ginger, coriander,

COLOUR

Coloured flowers add to the attraction of a potpourri.

Garden flowers dry easily if left hanging in a dry airy place for a few days.

Red flowers: *bergamot, rose, geranium, carnation*
Blue flowers: *borage, cornflower, forget-me-not, delphiniums, sage*
Yellow flowers: *cowslip, primrose, yarrow*
Orange flowers: *marigold, nasturtium, tansy*

SCENT

For scent we can choose from the leaves of basil, bay, bergamot, balm, melilot, mints, rosemary, sage, scented geraniums, southernwood, sweet cicely, tarragon, thymes, verbena and woodruff.

cinnamon and melilot, basil, rosemary, sandalwood, rose geranium, the lemon scented herbs and bergamot.

3 When the mixing is done, carefully pour each mixture into its own well-stoppered jar and hide it away from the light. Brown or green glass jars are the best to use.

Visit your cache every day and give each jar a stir with a wooden spoon, re-stopper quickly. Leave for a few weeks for the scents to blend and ripen before putting into potpourri jars.

QUICK AND EASY POTPOURRI

2 cups (500 ml) dried rose petals
2 cups (500 ml) dried lavender flowers
2 tbsp each dried lemon verbena leaves and dried rosemary
2 tbsp orris root powder
1/2 tsp powdered gum benzoin
2 drops lavender oil

1 Mix together all the ingredients but the last one. When nicely blended, add the oil a drop at a time, stirring continuously, to spread it through the mix evenly.

2 Tip the materials into a large jar, filling it only loosely and store in a dark, warm, dry place. Ideally you should visit it every day for the next five weeks to give it a good shake. This is important— impatience doesn't pay off.

3 Some people don't bother to do this but just rely on 6 to 8 weeks in the dark to mature the material and blend the scents.

The final potting should be in the prettiest and most imaginative container you can find. There are perforated ones made for the purpose but I find that to get the best from any potpourri it is best to take off the lid and shake the contents around at strategic moments. The perfume needs to be released to drift on the air. The fragrance is subtler than that of incense sticks which make it look as though you are trying too hard.

MINT AND MARIGOLD BLEND

These dry, clean scents are suitable for a man's room.

1/2 cup (125 ml) each dried pepper mint, basil and thyme leaves
1/2 cup (125 ml) marigold petals
1/2 cup (125 ml) orris root powder
4 drops oil of peppermint

Mix all ingredients together and keep in a sealed container for 6 weeks, shaking at least once a day before putting into a potpourri container.

LEMON AND MARIGOLD BLEND

1 cup (250 ml) each dried leaves of lemon balm and lemon verbena
1 cup (250 ml) each dried petals— marigold and chamomile flowers dried peel of a lemon—finely powdered
1/2 cup (125ml) orris root powder
6 drops lemon balm, lemon verbena or lemongrass oil.

Mix together and keep in a sealed container for 6 weeks, shaking each day before transferring to decorative pots.

Below: *Dried marigold and chamomile lowers with dried lemon peel and cinnamon sticks make a wonderful potpourri combination.*
Right: *Collecting the right ingredients for a potpourri is a sensuous pleasure.*

Helpful Hints

- *The herbs will lose their fragrance if exposed too often to the air so only lift the lid briefly to stir them to release their fragrance into the room.*
- *The scent of the citrus peel should not overpower the scent of the herbs.*
- *Rose petals and lavender flowers are the basis of most potpourris.*
  You can vary the overall effect by the addition of other herbs.
- *For sweet scent, add bergamot, violets and rose-scented geranium leaves.*
- *For a spicy, more masculine one, add bay leaves, lovage, thyme and sage.*
- *For a light, clean one, add costmary, eau-de-cologne mint, lemon verbena and melilot leaves.*
- *A quick way to scent a room is to wipe a few drops of essential oil over the light bulbs. The dried oil will have to be cleaned off if the bulbs are to give maximum light.*

Honey
Cider
Vinegar

Herbal Health & Medicine

Preparing Herbal Medicine

Herbs have been used as medicines since time out of mind. Their effects are proven by long experience and they do not have unexpected and unpleasant repercussions on the human body. Until the early years of the present century herbs were used as medicine as well as food in most parts of the world.

There are different ways of prescribing herbal medicines—the simplest one is by infusion—the making of "tea".

INFUSIONS

The traditional proportion is 30 g/1 oz fresh herb or 15 g/½ oz dried herb to 600 ml/1 pint or 2½ cups of boiling water for tea for drinking, and three or four times the amount of herb to water for making poultices or fomentations.

The water should be just off the boil when poured over the herbs and the container should be covered at once to prevent the volatile oils being dissipated in the steam. The infusion should be left to cool before drinking to allow the properties of the herb to be released.

Below Left: *Fresh and dry herbs are both important in herbal medicine.*
Right: *A simple way of making an infusion. Infusions are drunk fresh and are not stored.*

DECOCTION

The traditional proportions are the same as for an infusion.

A decoction is made by pouring cold water over the herb, bringing it to the boil and keeping it simmering until the liquid is reduced by one third. Stems, flowers and leaves will need about 20 minutes, seeds a little longer and barks and roots longer again.

Never use an aluminium saucepan. Instead of boiling the herbs a slow pan can be used I am told but have never tried it.

The amount made will provide enough dosage for several days. It should be kept covered in the refrigerator.

Infusions are taken in small cupful doses, three times a day; decoctions in wineglassful doses three times a day.

TINCTURE

A tincture is stronger than either an infusion or a decoction.

One teaspoon can take the place of a cupful of infusion or decoction.

Alcohol at 70 per cent proof is used in the preparation. Gin, vodka or brandy will do—if you can't find any at that strength buy some pure alcohol from a chemist. If it is more than 70 per cent proof dilute it with distilled water.

Method

1 Put some fresh chopped herb or half the amount of the dried one in a jar and cover it with alcohol. Seal the jar tightly and leave it in a cool place.

2 Visit the jar twice a day for two weeks. Lift it up and tap the base gently on the shelf or table on which it stands so as to agitate the contents. If you are afraid the jar might break, stand it on a folded newspaper and use that to soften the impact.

3 After two weeks strain the tincture into brown or green glass bottles, seal tightly, label with name and date of preparation and store in a cool dark place.

Dosage is from 5 to 15 drops taken in water, before meals, three times a day.

Because of the alcohol content, tinctures are not recommended for people with liver problems or when fever is present. They are good for stimulating bodily energy and giving warmth.

SYRUP

Make a base syrup by melting 450 g/1 lb sugar in 250 ml/1 cup of water and bringing it to the boil. You can also make a syrup by boiling up 5 parts honey to 1 part cider vinegar. Be careful, this can be tricky.

Add one part tincture to 3 parts syrup, bottle and store in the refrigerator.

Syrups are not recommended for diabetics.

Above: *Healing herb formulae always begin with dry plant material. Fresh herbs should be dried before they are used.*

Right: *The preparation of tinctures. Tinctures are extracts made with alcohol rather than water. They and remain potent longer. Shake the mixture every few days to encourage the alcohol to absorb the herbs' medicinal properties.*

Medicinal Herbs

ALOE

Aloe vera

Parts used: the thick gel found in the leaves

General: Every kitchen should have a potted aloe plant handy so that it is easy to cut off the thick, fleshy leaves and squeeze the clear gel onto an injury.

Arab traders carried aloe from Spain to Asia around the 6th century and used it to treat skin problems. The Chinese developed its use which was taken up by the West.

Contemporary herbalists use aloe in some of the same ways it was used almost 2,000 years ago—externally for burns and wounds.

Applications

wounds, burns, scalds, scrapes, sunburn, dry skin, fungal infections and insect bites

Gel: To help soothe wounds, burns, scalds and sunburn, and to help avoid infection. Clean the wound with soap and water then select a lower (older) leaf, cut several centimetres off, slice it lengthwise, apply the gel to the wound and allow it to dry.

Ointment. Cut the leaves and collect a large quantity of gel then boil it down to a thick paste. Store in a cool place and use as the fresh leaves.

Tonic: Mix 10 ml/2 tsp of gel with a glass of water or fruit juice. Take three times a day.

Inhalation: Use the gel in a steam inhalation for bronchial relief.

Caution: High internal doses of the leaves can cause vomiting.

ANGELICA

Angelica spp.

Parts used: roots, leaves—leaves from *A. archangelica;* roots from *A. archangelica* and *A. senensis*

During the 17th century, angelica was popular for colds and respiratory ailments.

When the colonists arrived in North America, they found many Indian tribes also using the herb to treat respiratory ailments, particularly tuberculosis.

Applications

respiratory ailments, digestive aid, arthritis, liver function, anaemia, menstrual irregularities

Tincture: Make from the leaves of *A. archangelica*. Take up to 3 ml/60 drops three times a day for colds, flu, bronchitis, and asthma. A tincture from the root of *A. archangelica* is good for catarrh and chesty coughs.

Infusion: Use 5 ml/1 tsp of powdered seeds or leaves per cup of boiling water. Steep 10 to 20 minutes.

An infusion of the leaves of *A. archangelica* taken in standard doses will help the digestion.

Compress: Make a compress and soak it in a hot diluted tincture made from the root of *A. archangelica* and apply to painful arthritic joints.

Essential oil: Mix 10 drops of angelica oil in 40 ml/2 tbsp of sunflower oil and massage arthritic or rheumatic joints.

Decoction: Use 5 ml/1 tsp of powdered roots of *A. senensis* per 250 ml/cup of water. Bring to a boil and simmer 2 minutes. Let stand 15 minutes.

Take for liver stagnation, anaemia and menstrual irregularities.

(LEMON) BALM

Melissa officinalis

Parts used: leaves

General: Bees love this fragrant herb, which explains its generic name, melissa —Greek for "bee."

The ancient Greek physician Dioscorides applied balm leaves to skin wounds and added the herb to wine to treat a variety of illnesses. The Roman naturalist Pliny used it to stop bleeding. During the 10th century, Arab doctors recommended balm for nervousness and anxiety.

Medieval Europeans also used balm for nervousness and anxiety. Melissa water, or Eau de Melisse, was a popular tranquilliser and sedative.

Balm contains chemicals (polyphenols) that help fight infections causing bacteria and eugenol, an anaesthetic, that helps relieve wound pain.

Applications
depression, tension, swellings, sores, insect bites, digestion

Compress: Make a hot compress using 10 ml/2 tsp of leaves per 250 ml/1 cup of water. Boil 10 minutes, strain and apply with a clean cloth to relieve painful swellings.

A relaxing bath: Tie a handful of balm in a cloth and run your bathwater over it. You'll love its lemony aroma and tranquillizing effect.

To treat wounds: To treat a minor cut, crush fresh balm leaves and apply them directly to the wound.

Tincture: Use 2.5 to 7.5 ml/$^1/_2$ to $1^1/_2$ tsp up to three times a day. Best made from fresh leaves. It has a similar action to the infusion but is stronger.

Infusion: For a light, lemony-tasting infusion to help soothe the stomach, fight infection, nervous exhaustion and depression or ease menstrual pain, use 2 tsp of leaves per 250 ml/1 cup of water. Steep 10 to 20 minutes. Drink up to 3 cups a day.

Ointment: For sores and insect bites.

Infused oil: Use as a warm massage oil to help relieve tension and depression.

BASIL

Ocimum basilicum

Parts used: leaves

In India, basil has long been revered as a sacred herb. The native species is even called *Ocimum sanctum*, "holy basil."

Basil's healing reputation has been mixed. The ancient Greek Dioscorides and the influential Roman doctor Galen both warned against taking basil internally, saying it caused insanity and spontaneous generation of internal worms.

But the Roman naturalist Pliny and Arab physicians 1,000 years later defended it as a great healer, as did the Chinese, who used it to treat stomach, kidney, and blood ailments.

Applications
acne, depression, itching skin

Infusion: Use 2 to 3 tsp of dried leaves per cup of boiling water. Steep 10 to 20 minutes. Apply with cotton wool to acne spots. Indian researchers have reported that basil kills bacteria when applied to the skin and have used basil oil successfully to treat acne.

Tincture: Use 5 ml/1 tsp up to three times a day.

Fresh leaves: Rub on insect bites to reduce inflammation and itching.

Essential oil: Add about 10 drops to a hot bath for nervous exhaustion or mental fatigue.

Caution: Basil should not be given in medicinal quantities to children under two.

BURDOCK

Arctium lappa

Parts used: leaves, root, seeds

Early Chinese physicians and India's traditional Ayurvedic healers used burdock as a remedy for colds, flu, throat infections, and pneumonia.

Later European herbalists prescribed burdock root for fever, eczema, psoriasis, acne, dandruff, gout, ringworm, skin infections, syphilis, gonorrhea, and problems associated with childbirth.

Contemporary herbalists recommend it for skin problems, wound treatment, urinary tract infection, arthritis, sciatica, ulcers, and anorexia nervosa.

Applications

skin disorders, sores, boils, fungal skin infections

Decoction: Boil 1 tsp of root in 3 cups of water for 30 minutes. Cool. Drink up to 3 cups a day. It has a sweet taste similar to celery root.

Use for skin disorders, especially boils, sores and dry skin. Use as a wash for acne and fungal skin infections.

Poultice: Apply a poultice made from the root to skin sores and ulcers. A poultice of leaves can be applied to bruises and skin inflammations.

CELERY

Apium graveolens

Parts used: seeds, root, stalk

Scientists have discovered a surprising number of healing uses for celery seed. They help relieve insomnia and high blood pressure.

Contemporary herbalists recommend celery as a diuretic, tranquilliser, sedative, and menstruation promoter, and as treatment for gout, arthritis, obesity and anxiety.

Applications

arthritis, hypertension, urinary disorders

Infusion: Try a pleasant-tasting infusion as a mild relaxant or to bring on menstruation. Use 1 to 2 tsp of freshly crushed seeds per 250 ml/cup of boiling water. Steep 10 to 20 minutes. Drink up to 3 cups a day.

An infusion of 1 tsp of crushed seeds to per cup of boiling water will clear the acid from joints and relieve the pain of arthritis.

Tincture: Use seeds to make the tincture and take 5 ml/1 tsp up to three times a day to relieve urinary tract infections.

A tincture from the root has been used in the past as a diuretic for hypertension and urinary disorders.

Essential oil: Dilute 10 drops in about 20 ml of sunflower oil and massage arthritic joints.

CHAMOMILE

Chamaemelum nobile & Matricaria recutita

Parts used: flowers

Chamomile is not one herb, but two German (or Hungarian) chamomile and Roman (or English) chamomile. The two plants are botanically unrelated, but they both produce the same light blue oil used in healing since ancient times.

The Greek physician Dioscorides and the Roman naturalist Pliny recommended chamomile to treat headaches and kidney, liver, and bladder problems. India's ancient Ayurvedic physicians used it similarly.

Germans have used chamomile since the dawn of history for digestive upsets and as a menstruation promoter and treatment for menstrual cramps.

Contemporary herbalists recommend chamomile externally to spur wound healing and treat inflammation, and internally for fever, digestive upsets, anxiety and insomnia.

Applications

insomnia, anxiety, stress, tension, irritable bowel syndrome, insect bites, strained eyes, hayfever, bronchitis, mouth inflammations

Bath: For a relaxing bath, tie a handful of chamomile flowers in a cloth and run your bathwater over it.

The herb soothes the central nervous system; when you feel anxious take a hot "chamomile" bath.

Infusion: For a refreshing infusion, use 2 to 3 heaped teaspoons of flowers per cup of boiling water. Steep 10 to 20 minutes.

Drink a cup at night for insomnia, anxiety or stress. Also take for irritable bowel syndrome.

Use as a mouthwash for any ulcers or inflammations.

For cuts, scrapes, or burns, brew a strong infusion, cool it, and apply in compresses.

Tincture: Use 5 ml/1 tsp up to three times a day.

Dissolve 5-10 drops of tincture in warm water for use as an eyewash to treat strained eyes.

Inhalation: Add 2 tsp of flowers to boiling water and inhale for hay fever or bronchitis.

Essential oil: Chamomile oil applied to the skin reduces the time it takes burns to heal.

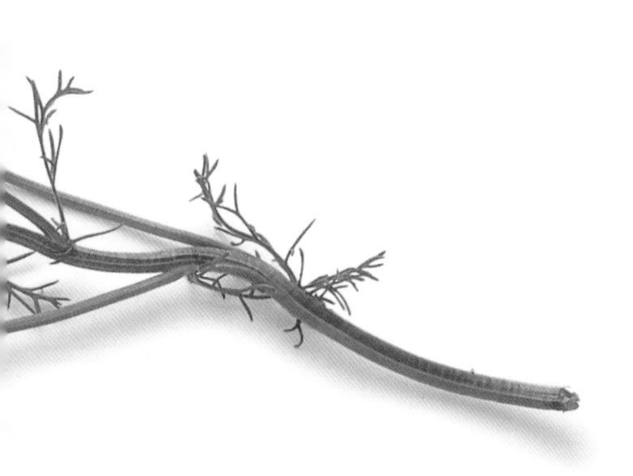

COMFREY

Symphytum officinale

Parts used: roots, leaves

The early Greeks first used comfrey root externally to treat wounds, believing it encouraged torn flesh to grow back together.

Comfrey paste hardens like plaster, and cloths soaked in it were often wrapped around broken bones. When the paste dried, the result was a primitive but effective cast. This treatment earned comfrey the popular names "knitbone" and "boneset".

Comfrey contains a chemical (allantoin) which encourages cartilage, bone and muscle cells to grow. When the herb is crushed and applied to an injured limb the allantoin is absorbed through the skin speeding up the healing process.

Be sure to wash wounds thoroughly with soap and water before applying comfrey or the rapid healing process may trap dirt and infection.

Applications

minor fractures, bone or muscle damage, bruises, sprains

For wound treatment: Comfrey roots are preferable to the leaves. Roots contain more than twice as much allantoin.

Poultice: Purée the leaves and apply to minor fractures not set in plaster—broken toes, ribs etc.

Infused oil: Use for arthritic joints, bruises and sprains.

CONEFLOWER, PURPLE

Echinacea spp.

Parts used: root

Coneflower was the American Plains Indians' primary medicine. They applied root poultices to all manner of wounds, insect bites, stings and snakebites. They used it as a mouthwash for painful teeth and gums and drank it as tea to treat colds, smallpox, measles, mumps, and arthritis.

In 1870, a patent-medicine purveyor, Dr. H. C. F. Meyer of Nebraska, used it in his Meyer's Blood Purifier. He promoted the remedy as "an absolute cure" for rattlesnake bites, blood poisoning, and a host of other ills.

Contemporary herbalists are enthusiastic about coneflower for its anti-fungal and anti-bacterial properties. The herb contains a natural antibiotic (echinacoside), which is comparable to penicillin in that it has broad-spectrum activity.

Applications

infection, inflammation, common catarrh and colds, food poisoning, snake bite, sore throat, wounds

Decoction: Use to fight infection or as possible treatment for arthritis.

To make a decoction, bring 2 tsp of root material per 250 ml/1 cup of water to a boil, then simmer 15 minutes. Take 10 ml doses every 2-3 hours for acute infections.

Bathe the infected area.

Tincture: Take 2-5 ml doses every 2-3 hours for chills and colds. Take in 10 ml doses for snake bite and food poisoning. For a sore throat gargle with 10 ml in a glass of warm water.

DANDELION

Taraxacum officinale

Parts used: leaves, root

Chinese physicians have prescribed dandelion since ancient times to treat colds, bronchitis, pneumonia, hepatitis, boils, ulcers, obesity, dental problems, itching and internal injuries.

Tenth-century Arab physicians were the first to recognize that dandelion increases urine production.

Contemporary herbalists recommend dandelion leaves almost exclusively as a diuretic for weight loss, premenstrual syndrome, menstrual discomforts, swollen feet and high blood pressure.

Applications

diuretic, cleanser, warts

Fresh stalks: The sap from the fresh plant can be effective against warts. Apply directly from the stem or the root.

Infusion: Use 15g/½ oz of dried leaves per 250 ml/cup of boiling water. Steep 10 minutes. Drink 3 cups a day.

Use for cleansing toxic conditions and as a digestive stimulant.

Tincture: For a root decoction, gently boil 2 to 3 tsp of powdered root per 250 ml/cup of water for 15 minutes. Cool. Drink up to 3 cups a day or 5 to 10 ml/1 to 2 tsp up to 3 times a day.

Use for toxic conditions such as acne and eczema.

Diuretic: Diuretics can help eliminate water weight, but should not be used for permanent weight control.

The diuretic may also help relieve the bloated feeling of premenstrual syndrome.

If you're using dandelion leaves as a diuretic (for premenstrual syndrome or high blood pressure) or digestive aid, take it as a root decoction, or tincture. The taste is reasonably pleasant.

Diuretics deplete the body of potassium, an essential nutrient. People taking diuretics should be sure to eat foods high in potassium, such as bananas and fresh vegetables.

Dandelion causes no potassium loss because the herb itself is high in potassium.

Caution: Dandelion may cause skin rash in sensitive persons.

FENNEL

Foeniculum officinale

Parts used: seeds, root

During the third century B.C., Hippocrates prescribed fennel to treat infant colic. Four hundred years later, Dioscorides called it an appetite suppressant and recommended the seeds to nursing mothers to boost milk production.

The Roman naturalist Pliny included fennel in 22 remedies. He noted that some snakes rubbed against the plant after shedding their skins and soon after, their glazed eyes cleared. Pliny took this as a sign that fennel cured human eye problems, including blindness.

Contemporary herbalists recommend fennel as a digestive aid, milk promoter, expectorant, eyewash, and buffer in herbal laxative blends.

Applications
digestive aid, gum disorders, sore throat, nervous stomach

Seeds: As a digestive aid, chew a handful of seeds.

Infusion: To make a pleasant, liquorice flavoured infusion, use 1 to 2 tsp of bruised seeds per 250 ml/cup of boiling water. Steep 10 minutes. Drink up to 3 cups a day.

Take for indigestion, acidity, colic or griping pains. It has a carminative action.

Tincture: Take 2.5 to 5 ml/½ to 1 tsp up to three times a day.

Like most other aromatic herbs, fennel appears to relax the smooth muscle lining of the digestive tract thus making it an antispasmodic.

FEVERFEW

Tanacetum parthenium

Parts used: leaves

During the Middle Ages, the Greek name for the herb, "parthenion" was replaced by "featherfoil" because of its feathery leaf borders. "Featherfoil" eventually became feverfew.

Once feverfew acquired its name, herbalists decided it was a fever treatment and recommended it for other ailments, particularly headache.

Applications
migraine headaches, period pain

Fresh leaves: For migraine control, chew two fresh (or frozen) leaves a day, or take a pill or capsule containing 85 milligrams of leaf material. If feverfew capsules do not provide benefit after a few weeks, don't give up on the herb. "Feverfew" pills and capsules contain only trace amounts of the herb.

Tincture: Feverfew is a prophylactic. You take the remedy daily in order to prevent migraine attacks. Take 5 to 10 drops every 30 minutes if you think a migraine is coming on.

Infusion: Use 2.5 to 5 ml/½ to 1 tsp per 250 ml/cup of boiling water. Steep 5 to 10 minutes. Drink up to 2 cups a day. Take feverfew in the form of an infusion to help lower blood pressure, as a digestive aid, or to help bring on menstruation.

Caution: Chewing the leaves can cause mouth ulcers.
If you are taking any kind of blood thinning drug avoid feverfew.

GARLIC

Allium sativum

Parts used: bulb

In the world's oldest surviving medical text, the Ebers Papyrus, garlic was an ingredient in 22 remedies for headache, insect and scorpion bites, menstrual discomforts, intestinal worms, tumours, and heart problems.

The Greek physician Hippocrates recommended it for infections, wounds, cancer, leprosy, and digestive problems. Pliny listed it in 61 remedies.

During World War I, British, French, and Russian army physicians treated infected battle wounds with garlic juice. They also prescribed garlic to prevent and treat amoebic dysentery.

Garlic's strong odour is due to sulphur containing compounds which account for most of its medicinal properties.

Applications

warts, high cholesterol, digestive disorders, corns, fungal infections, high blood pressure, skin infections, chest problems

Infusion: Chop six cloves per 250 ml/cup of cool water and steep 6 hours.

Tincture: Soak 1 cup (250 ml) of crushed cloves per 2 l of brandy, shake daily for two weeks, then take up to 60 ml/3 tbsp a day.

Fresh cloves: One medium-sized garlic clove packs the anti-bacterial punch of about 100,000 units of penicillin. Depending on the type of infection, oral penicillin doses typically range from 600,000 to 1.2 million units. The equivalent in garlic would be about 6 to 12 cloves. It's best to chew 3 cloves at a time, two to four times a day.

Rub fresh onto acne and mash to use on warts.

To help reduce blood pressure and cholesterol, eating three to ten cloves of fresh garlic a day is recommended.
Garlic must be chewed, chopped, bruised, or crushed to transform its medicinally inert allicin into antibiotic allicin.

Caution: May irritate the stomach.

To eliminate garlic breath, try chewing traditional herbal breath fresheners: parsley, fennel, or fenugreek.

GINGER

Zingiber officinalis

Parts used: root

Ginger appeared prominently in China's first great herbal, the Pen Tsao Ching (Classic of Herbs), compiled by Shen Nung around 3000 B.C. Shen Nung recommended ginger for colds, fever, chills, tetanus and leprosy.

Chinese sailors chewed ginger to prevent seasickness, and the physicians prescribed it for arthritis and kidney problems. Chinese women still drink ginger tea for menstrual cramps, morning sickness, and other gynaecological problems.

Ginger is also considered an antidote to shellfish poisoning, which is why Chinese fish and seafood dishes are often seasoned with the herb.

Applications

motion sickness, nausea, morning sickness, digestive aid, colds

Capsules: For motion sickness, the recommended dose is 1,500 milligrams 30 minutes before travel. Commercial ginger capsules are usually most convenient.

Also used for morning sickness.

Tea: Use tea as a digestive aid to help treat colds and flu, nausea, morning sickness, or arthritis. To make ginger tea, use 2 tsp of powdered or grated root per cup of boiling water. Steep 10 minutes.

Tincture: 2-10 drops a dose for nausea, indigestion and menstrual cramps.

Decoction: For colds and flu add 1-2 slices of fresh ginger to a cup of water and simmer for 10 minutes.

MARSHMALLOW

Althaea officinalis

Parts used: root or leaves

Marshmallow was a food before it was a medicine.

The plant's history as a healer goes back to Hippocrates, who prescribed a decoction of marshmallow roots to treat bruises and blood loss from wounds. Four hundred years later, the Greek physician Dioscorides recommended marshmallow root poultices for insect bites and stings and prescribed the decoction for toothache and vomiting and as an antidote to poisons.

Tenth-century Arab physicians used mallow leaf poultices to treat inflammations.

The botanical name is taken from the Greek word, *altho*, meaning "to heal".

The spongy material in marshmallow roots is called mucilage. When it comes in contact with water, it swells and forms a gel.

Applications

cuts and wounds, respiratory system, immune system, cuts, scrapes, burns, gastritis, peptic ulcers

Gel: To prepare for external use, chop the root very fine and add enough water to make a gooey gel. Apply the gel directly to superficial wounds, cuts, scrapes or sunburn.

Decoction: Enjoy a sweet decoction to take advantage of marshmallow's soothing potential and possible infection fighting abilities. To make a decoction, gently boil 2.5 to 5 ml/½ to 1 tsp of chopped or crushed root per cup of water for 10 to 15 minutes. Drink up to 3 cups a day.

Taken internally, it helps relieve upset stomach and the respiratory rawness associated with sore throat, cough, colds, flu and bronchitis.

MEADOWSWEET

Filipendula ulmaria

Parts Used: leaves, flower tops

During the Middle Ages, meadowsweet's delicate almond fragrance made it a popular air freshener, or "strewing herb". It was also used to ease fever and pains.

We owe aspirin to the aromatic meadowsweet.

In 1839, a German chemist discovered meadowsweet flower buds contained salicin. Salicin has powerful pain-relieving (analgesic), fever-reducing, and anti-inflammatory properties.

In 1853, German chemists working with an extract of meadowsweet synthesised acetylsalicylic acid. The new drug was named aspirin from the old botanical name for the herb. They called the new "wonder drug" aspirin, after *Spiraea ulmaria*, the old botanical name for the herb.

In the late 1890s, a German chemist, Hoffman, became upset because his father's rheumatoid arthritis medication brought him so little relief. He worked at the Fredrich Bayer pharmaceutical company and when he came upon the old reports about aspirin he prepared the drug.

Applications

headache, rheumatic pains, feverish colds, muscles, aches, digestive upsets, childhood diarrhoea

Infusion: For a pleasantly astringent infusion, use 1 to 2 tsp of dried herb per 250 ml/1 cup of boiling water. Steep 10 minutes. Take for headaches, muscle aches, feverish colds, rheumatic pains and upset stomachs.

Tincture: Tinctures provide greater pain relief.

Compress: Soak pads in a diluted tincture and place on arthritic joints.

MINT

Mentha spp.

Parts used: leaves, flower tops

All the mints were considered one plant until 1696, when British botanist John Ray differentiated them.

Mint was listed as a stomach soother in the Ebers Papyrus, the world's oldest surviving medical text.

Chinese and Ayurvedic physicians used mint as a tonic and digestive aid and as a treatment for colds, cough, and fever.

Contemporary herbalists recommend peppermint externally for itching and inflammations, and internally as a digestive aid and treatment for menstrual cramps, motion sickness, morning sickness, colds, cough, flu, congestion, headache, heartburn, fever and insomnia. Peppermint is more potent than spearmint.

Applications

digestive aid, decongestant, infection prevention, itching, nausea, inflamed joints, travel sickness, wounds

Essential oil: For wounds, burns and scalds apply a few drops of peppermint oil directly to the affected area.

A few drops of oil in water can be applied to the skin to relieve irritations and itching and to repel mosquitoes.

Inhalation: Put some fresh leaves in boiling water. Inhale to relieve nasal congestion.

Infusion: For a decongestant or digestive infusion, use 1 to 2 tsp of dried herb per 250 ml/cup of boiling water. Steep 10 minutes. Peppermint has a sharper taste than spearmint, and cools the mouth.

Tincture: Take one quarter to 1 tsp up to three times a day.

For a herbal bath, fill a cloth bag with a few handfuls of dried or fresh herb and let the water run over it.

Caution: If mints cause minor discomforts, such as stomach upset or diarrhoea, use less or stop using it.
Because mint can irritate the mucous membranes it should not be given to children for more than a week without a break.

MOTHERWORT

Leonurus cardiaca

Parts used: leaves, flowers, stems

The ancient Greeks and Romans used motherwort for both physical and emotional heart problems—palpitations and depression.

In ancient China, motherwort was reputed to promote longevity. In Europe, motherwort first became known as a treatment for cattle diseases. Chinese herbalists use the species mainly for menstrual disorders.

Applications

blood pressure, menopausal syndrome, sore eyes, tranquilliser

Infusion: For a tranquillizing, uterine stimulating, blood pressure-lowering infusion, use 2 tsp of dried herb per cup of boiling water. Steep 10 minutes. Drink up to 2 cups a day, a tablespoon at a time.

Also use as a tonic for menopausal syndrome and anxiety.

Motherwort tastes very bitter. Add sugar, honey, and lemon, or mix it into a herbal tea to improve the flavour.

Tincture: Take 1/2 to 1 tsp up to twice a day.

Decoction: Use a weak decoction for conjunctivitis and tired eyes.

Caution: Do not use during pregnancy as motherwort stimulates the uterus.

Some people develop a rash from contact with this plant.

(POT) MARIGOLD

Calendula officinalis

Parts used: petals

The ancients used marigold to "strengthen the heart" and it was also highly regarded for treating smallpox and measles.

The petals can be applied externally to help in a wide range of skin problems. Pot marigold is used today in many homeopathic remedies.

Applications

menstrual disorders, inflammation, gastritis, mouth ulcers and gum problems, scalds, sunburn, dry skin, chilblains, anxiety, dry eczema, digestion

Tincture: Take for menstrual disorders, especially period pain or irregular periods and to aid digestion.

Mouthwash: Use the infusion as a mouth wash to treat mouth ulcers or gum problems.

Infusion: Use the infusion for period pain, gastritis, or for menopausal problems.

Ointment: Apply to relieve dry skin, sunburn, scalds, inflammation of the skin or dry eczema.

Infused oil: Use for chilblains

Essential oil: Use 5-10 drops of the oil added to a bath if you are feeling anxious.

ROSEMARY

Rosmarinus officinalis

Parts used: leaves

The ancients used rosemary as they used all aromatic, preservative herbs—for head, respiratory, and gastro-intestinal problems. Chinese physicians mixed it with ginger to treat headaches, indigestion, insomnia, and malaria.

In World War II, French nurses burned a mixture of rosemary leaves and juniper berries in the wards.

Contemporary herbalists say rosemary stimulates the circulatory, digestive, and nervous systems. They recommend it for headaches, indigestion, depression, muscle pain, as a gargle to treat bad breath, externally to prevent premature baldness, and in baths for relaxation.

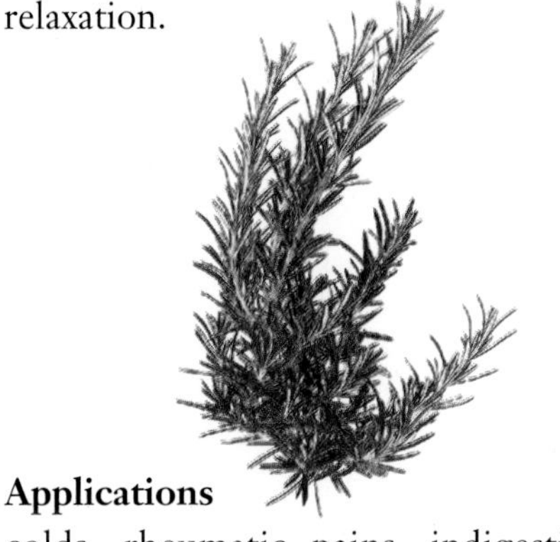

Applications

colds, rheumatic pains, indigestion, fatigue, sprains, dandruff

Infusion: For a pleasantly aromatic infusion to settle the stomach, clear a stuffed nose, relieve rheumatic pains or help indigestion use 1 tsp of crushed herb per cup of boiling water. Steep 10 to 15 minutes. Drink up to 3 cups a day.

Use as a hair rinse to combat dandruff.

Tincture: Use 1.5 to 2.5 ml/¼ to ½ tsp up to three times a day.

Compress: Soak a pad in a hot infusion and use for sprains. Alternate with cold ice packs every two or three minutes.

Essential oil: A few drops in a hot bath will relieve aching limbs.

SKULLCAP

Scutellaria spp.

Parts used: leaves

Chinese physicians use Asian skullcap *(S. baicalensis)* as a tranquilliser/sedative and treatment for convulsions.

It was first brought to the attention of physicians in the West in 1772 as a cure for rabies.

The herb was used primarily as a tranquilliser/sedative for insomnia and nervousness, and for treatment of "intermittent fever" (malaria), convulsions and the delirium tremors of advanced alcoholism.

Contemporary herbalists recommend skullcap as a tranquilliser for insomnia, nervous tension, premenstrual syndrome, and drug and alcohol withdrawal symptoms.

Applications

tranquilliser, nervous disorders, insomnia, premenstrual tension

Infusion: For a tranquillizing infusion, use 2 tsp of dried herb per 250 ml/cup boiling water. Steep 10 to 15 minutes. Drink up to three times a day for nervous exhaustion, over-anxiety and premenstrual tension.

Skullcap tastes bitter; adding honey, sugar, and lemon will make it palatable.

Tincture: Potent for calming the nerves. Combine with lemon balm for nervous stress.

THYME

Thymus vulgaris

Parts used: leaves, flower tops

The Romans used thyme medicinally as a cough remedy, digestive aid, and treatment for intestinal worms.

It was used as an antiseptic during plagues, and those troubled by "melancholia" (depression) were advised to sleep on thyme-stuffed pillows.

By the late 17th century, apothecary shops were selling thyme oil as an antiseptic under the name oil of origanum.

From the mid-19th century through World War I, thyme enjoyed great popularity as an antiseptic.

Contemporary herbalists recommend thyme externally for wound disinfection and internally for indigestion, sore throat, laryngitis, cough, whooping cough and nervousness.

Applications

sore throat, coughs, infection, unsettled stomach, insect bites, antiseptic

Infusion: For an infusion to help settle the stomach, soothe a cough, or possibly help relieve menstrual symptoms, use 2 tsp of dried herb per 250 ml/cup of boiling water. Steep 10 minutes. Drink up to 3 cups a day. Thyme is pleasantly aromatic with a faint clove-like aftertaste.

Use as a gargle for a sore throat.

Tincture: Take 5 ml/1 teaspoon up to three times a day.

Once wounds have been thoroughly washed, apply a few drops of thyme tincture as an antiseptic.

Essential oil: Add 10 drops to 25ml/1$\frac{1}{2}$ tablespoons of water and apply to infected wounds and insect bites.

Caution: Thyme oil may cause a rash in sensitive individuals.

Do not use therapeutic doses of thyme during pregnancy.

VALERIAN

Valeriana officinalis

Parts used: rhizome, roots

Valerian has a disagreeable odour, and ancient Greek and Roman authorities called it "fu". The term Valerian appeared around the 10th century, derived from the Latin "valere", to be strong.

Dioscorides recommended valerian as a diuretic and antidote to poisons. Pliny considered it a pain reliever. Galen prescribed it as a decongestant. By the time the plant's name became valerian, European herbalists considered it a panacea and also called it "All-heal".

During World War I, Europeans afflicted with overwrought nerves from artillery bombardment frequently took valerian.

All parts of valerian contain chemicals that have sedative properties known as valepotriates, but they occur in highest concentration in the roots.

Applications

insomnia, muscle cramp, wounds, anxiety, blood pressure

Infusion: As a potential sedative infusion for anxiety and insomnia, use 2 tsp of powdered root per cup of water. Steep 10 to 15 minutes. Drink 1 cup before bed. Valerian tastes unpleasant. Add sugar, honey, and lemon. Use on wounds and for drawing splinters.

Tincture: Take half to 5 ml/1 tsp before bed for insomnia. Can be added to other herbs such as hyssop where anxiety has contributed to high blood pressure.

Compress: Soak a pad in the tincture and apply to cramped muscles.

VERVAIN

Verbena officinalis

Parts used: leaves, flowers, roots

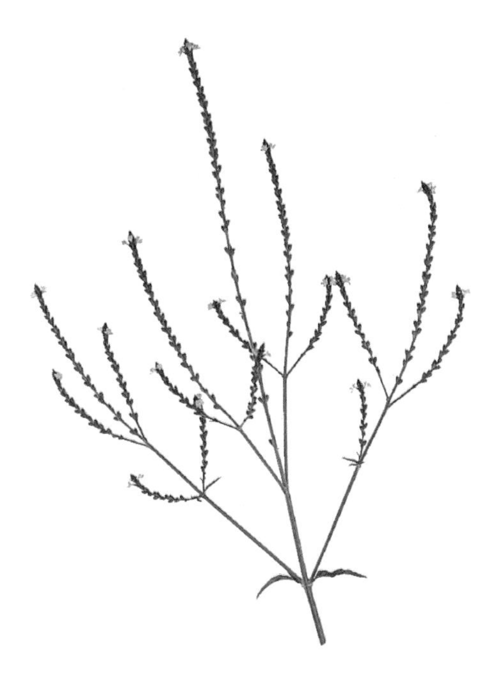

Vervain acts like a mild aspirin, helping to relieve minor pains and inflammations.

The Romans carried vervain throughout Europe, where it became especially popular among the Druids, who used it in magic spells.

During the Middle Ages, vervain became a popular acne remedy. Those with pimples stood outside at night holding a handful of the herb wrapped in a cloth.

Contemporary herbalists recommend vervain as a tranquilliser, expectorant, menstruation promoter, and treatment for headaches, fever, depression, seizures, wounds, dental cavities, and gum disease.

Applications

inflammation and pain relief, headaches, nervous tension, depression, sore gums, insomnia, bruises

Infusion: For a very bitter infusion using leaves and flowers to help treat headache, nervous tension, mild arthritis, and other minor pains, use 2 tsp of dried herb per 250 ml/cup of boiling water. Steep 10 to 15 minutes. Drink up to 3 cups a day. Mask vervain's bitterness with sugar, honey, and lemon.

Use as a mouthwash for ulcers and soft gums.

Tincture: Use 5 ml/1 teaspoon up to three times a day.
Take for nervous exhaustion and depression.

Poultice: Apply for insect bites, sprains and bruises.

Ointment: Use for eczema and weeping sores.

YARROW

Achillea millefolium

Parts used: leaves, stems, flower tops

Yarrow contains substances that help stop bleeding and have pain-relieving and anti-inflammatory properties helpful in wound treatment. It is also a digestive aid, menstrual remedy, and mild sedative.

Dioscorides, a physician attached to the Roman legions, recommended rubbing the crushed plant on wounds.

Contemporary herbalists recommend yarrow as "an herbal Band-Aid" and prescribe it for fevers, urinary tract infections, and as a digestive aid.

Applications

wounds, digestive aid, menstrual cramps, nose bleed, hayfever

Infusion: For a tranquillizing infusion, to help aid digestion or help treat menstrual cramps, use 2 tsp of dried herb per cup of boiling water. Steep 10 to 15 minutes. Drink up to 3 cups a day. Yarrow tastes tangy and bitter; to improve flavour, add honey, sugar, or lemon.

To help promote healing, apply it externally to clean wounds, inflammations and eczema.

Inhalation: Use fresh leaves in boiling water for hay fever and mild asthma.

Leaves: Stop a nose bleed by inserting a leaf in the nostril.

Press fresh leaves and flower tops into cuts before washing and bandaging them.

Caution: Avoid during pregnancy. High doses can turn urine dark brown. Do not be alarmed.

Herbal First Aid

The home can be a dangerous place—we fall off step-ladders and bruise ourselves—trip over obstacles and sprain an ankle—gash ourselves with knives and garden tools—burn, scald and sunbake ourselves—get bitten by insects— eat unwisely and develop indigestion and headaches—and have been known to take unwise liberties with electrical appliances. Shock, bruises, sprains and strains, cuts, wounds, burns and scalds make domestic dramas. It helps if we are ready for them and keep remedies in stock.

SHOCK

1. Rescue Remedy.
One of the Dr. Edward Bach Flower Remedies—can be bought in liquid form or as pills. I like the liquid best.

For severe shock the neat liquid is wiped across the lips, the gums and the wrists and a touch of it is given behind the ears. For mild shock 4 drops in a cup of cold water sipped slowly will restore equilibrium in a surprisingly short time. The pills are slipped under the tongue.

2. A packet of dried chamomile flowers or some bought chamomile tea bags will make a quick drink of soothing tea.

BRUISES AND SPRAINS

1. Arnica in homeopathic potency 6x for shakes and shock. 2 doses should be enough. One immediately and one half an hour later.

2. A tube of arnica cream—not to be used if the skin is broken.

3 . A jar of comfrey ointment—for gently smoothing over the sore area. Or a small bottle of home-made comfrey oil.

4. A small bottle of cider vinegar. Used, diluted, to bathe the injury and to soak a cloth which can be wrapped around it.

Use small bottles for storage. When the crisis has past they can be replenished with fresh remedies.

CUTS, WOUNDS AND GRAZES

1. A small jar of honey. No germ can live in honey. Use as a disinfectant.

2. Fresh yarrow leaves will stop bleeding. A pinch of dried yarrow leaves moistened with honey is effective.

3. Calendula (marigold) ointment which is antiseptic and healing.

BURNS AND SCALDS

1. A small bottle of nettle extract (sold as "Urtica"). A few drops in water is said to be enough to ease the pain. I always apply it neat—and fast. The pain goes almost at once and there is rarely any sign of a scar.

2. Aloe vera.

Herbal remedies can treat a variety of ailments. A basic supply of remedies should be kept in a medicine cupboard for emergency use.

HEADACHES

A small bottle containing 3 drops essential oil of lavender in some almond oil. Rub into the temples.

MIGRAINE

Keep a few feverfew leaves wrapped in foil in the freezer ready for chewing as soon as the first sign appears. If you can't stand the taste buy feverfew pills or capsules.

SUNBURN

Aloe gel is best. Snap a leaf in half and squeeze the cut ends to extract the gel which should be smoothed all over the affected area and left to dry.

You can make your own ointment by collecting gel and boiling it down into a thick paste. Pot it and keep in a cool place.

INSECT BITES

- hyssop oil or lotion
- lavender oil
- calendula ointment
- plantain poultice

HERBS TO GROW AND DRY FOR POULTICES

I use "poultice" as a blanket term to mean either fresh mashed herbs applied directly to a wound or sting, or dried herbs made into a paste with water and used in the same way, or fresh or dried water-heated herbs, enclosed in gauze and applied either hot or cold to a troubled area.

A poultice can disinfect, draw out poison and stop bleeding.

By accelerating the circulation and reducing inflammation it helps the body in its natural work of healing.

Comfrey, elder flowers, golden seal, lime flowers, marigold flowers, plantain, St. John's wort and yarrow are all herbs to have on hand, fresh or dried for poultices for wounds, burns and bruises.

Plantain is particularly good for insect bites.

Golden seal for skin ulcers.

Elderflowers, lime flowers, St. John's wort and yarrow for wounds and burns.

Always clean a wound before applying a poultice.

For the making of herbal oils to use as liniments for tired and sore muscles.

THE COMMON COLD

We cannot expect to escape accidents in the home and we can be certain that, at some time, we are going to suffer from the common cold.

Herbs for the Common Cold

It has to be faced; we have not found a cure for the common cold—the virus gets into the cells of the body where it cannot be reached by antibiotic drugs. All we can do is to try to nip it in the bud before it takes hold—if we don't succeed there is no choice but to let it run its course and to do our best to alleviate the symptoms.

As soon as the onset of a cold is suspected take some large doses of natural vitamin C and leave milk and eggs out of the diet—they encourage the creation of mucus. Eat plenty of onions.

Drink honey dissolved in hot water with the addition of some lemon juice and ground ginger or a tea made from equal parts elderflowers, hyssop and mint. Take these drinks hot every two hours. Sit with your feet in a mustard bath for 10 to 15 minutes. A small tin of bought mustard powder in a bowl of water large enough to take the feet comfortably will do.

If the cold is not averted and the throat becomes sore, gargle with some weak sage tea. Thyme tea is good too. To clear catarrh, inhale the steam rising from a bowl of hot water containing some eucalyptus oil—essential oil if you have it but the ordinary one will do. Make a towel tent to enclose your head and the bowl and inhale deeply through the nose. You will probably have had enough by ten minutes.

If the inflammation goes down to the chest or the bronchial tubes you will be forced to cough to clear the mucus. Do not take proprietary medicines which suppress coughing—you want to get rid of the mucus.

Drink tea made from angelica, cowslip, elecampane, horehound or thyme—all good expectorants.

Leave a sliced onion to soak in honey overnight, strain off the juice and take in large teaspoonful doses three or four times the next day.

The herbal pharmacy

Herbal Health

Hippocrates, who lived in the time before Christ and is often called the "father of medicine", categorised all herbs and foods by fundamental quality - hot, cold, dry or damp - and good health was maintained by keeping them in balance.

HERBS AND DIET

Hippocrates said "Let foods be your medicine" and classified them into hot, dry, damp or cold categories, each category having a different effect on the body. Balanced eating was important. Too much hot, dry food and there was trouble with the digestion and liver, too many cold, moist ones and catarrh developed.

He stressed the need for harmony in the body, found in a balance between matter and energy—"ease"—when it was lost there was "disease".

His categories tied in with the Greek concept of the world being made up from four elements: earth, air, fire and water. These elements related to the four seasons: cold, dry, damp, hot, and from there to the bodily humours and temperaments—the phlegmatic, melancholic, sanguine and choleric. Diagnosis of illness depended on an understanding of the "humours" and treatment on knowledge of the herbs needed to cure the condition.

The Greeks and Romans wrote herbals—Claudius Galen in the second century A.D. wrote the famous DE SIMPLICIBUS which influenced medicine for many, many years. He too advocated "balanced" eating—as did the ancient Chinese, Indians and Persians. Ayurvedic (ancient Indian) treatment categorises food according to taste—sweet, sour, salty, pungent, bitter, astringent. They act on the "humours" of the body—phlegm, bile and wind. A good mixture of them all is needed to keep the body healthy.

Sweet tastes, including rice and cashew nuts, should be avoided when there is too much water or phlegm in the body.

Sour tastes such as lemons and spinach decrease wind and increase bile.

Salty tastes retain water and release phlegm.

Pungent tastes such as horseradish and basil reduce phlegm and increase wind. They are stimulating and warming.

Bitter tastes such as chicory stimulate the appetite and reduce phlegm.

Astringent tastes such as sage decrease bile and phlegm and dry loose bowels and excessive menstruation.

But knowing this is merely scratching the surface. The Way of the Ayurveda consists of much more than treatment by food and herbs.

The Ayurvedic practitioner treats the whole person and not the disease which is currently being suffered. The treatment works slowly—as all holistic treatments do—the body is put back into balance and harmony enabling the mind to rest in equilibrium, clear, peaceful and centred.

CHINESE HERBAL MEDICINE

The ancient Chinese had a slightly different theory. Instead of tastes they had "elements"—not four like the Greeks, but five—earth, fire, water, wood and metal, which they used to interpret the relationship between man and the earth on which he lives.

The Chinese use sweet, sour, salty, bitter and pungent herbs to treat illness. Their concern is to see that all the elements in the body are in balance—too much of one and too little of another spells trouble.

The balance between yin—the dark, cold female element and yang—the white, hot male element is essential. The vital energy that flows through the body is yang—blood and the body fluids are yin.

Through all ancient medicine runs the belief that links between man and the natural world are basic—that belief lives on in herbal medicine, which, after a long time in the wilderness, is coming into its own again.

HERBAL TEAS FOR HEALTH

There are many more herbs that can be used to make remedial teas—these are some of the garden herbs which make tea which can be drunk for pleasure as well as healing.

Angelica: Drink it if you feel a cold coming on or you feel "rheumaticky".

Balm: Unsweetened this lemony drink will ease a cold or headache.

Basil: When you get the shivers for no apparent reason make a tea from the leaves and the flowering tips—5 g/¼ oz of herb to 125 ml of near boiling water and sit quietly and drink it after a meal.

Bergamot: A strong brew makes a gargle for a sore throat.

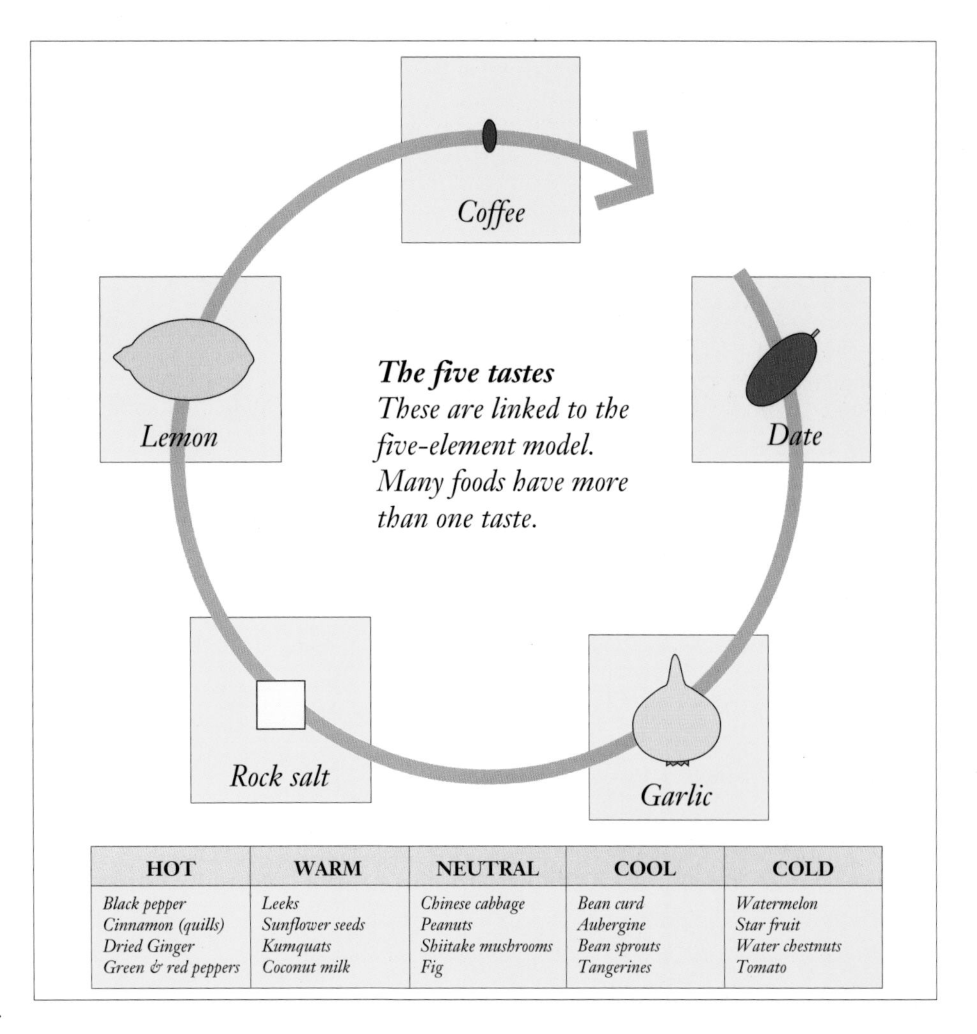

The five tastes
These are linked to the five-element model. Many foods have more than one taste.

HOT	WARM	NEUTRAL	COOL	COLD
Black pepper	*Leeks*	*Chinese cabbage*	*Bean curd*	*Watermelon*
Cinnamon (quills)	*Sunflower seeds*	*Peanuts*	*Aubergine*	*Star fruit*
Dried Ginger	*Kumquats*	*Shiitake mushrooms*	*Bean sprouts*	*Water chestnuts*
Green & red peppers	*Coconut milk*	*Fig*	*Tangerines*	*Tomato*

Borage: The ancients claimed that "borage maketh the mind glad" and since the plant is rich in mineral salts, potassium and calcium, who's arguing? A cucumber-tasting tea made from the leaves and flowers. It will cleanse the blood and enliven the system.

Catmint: Tea made from the leaves and flowers can help to sweat out a chill, relieve stomach wind and hiccups and bring on delayed menstruation.

Chamomile: This is one of the great soothers. It eases upset stomachs, strained nerves and prevents nightmares.
It is equally good for children cutting teeth or suffering from ear-ache and the harassed parents looking after them.

Golden rod: Tastes of aniseed and helps with high blood pressure.

Lovage: Good for the burps.

Mint: Good for a bad digestion.

Parsley: Parsley is good for digestion and the relief of cystitis and menstrual cramps. The tea is made from the leaves not the seeds.

Rosemary: When nerves are strained and a headache won't go away try some rosemary tea It has a reputation for being able to strengthen the memory.

Sage: Sage tea is good for depression, for sharpening the mental facilities and aiding the memory. It contains oestrogen and will tone up the female reproductive system. It also make a good gargle for a sore throat.

Thyme: A good bracing tonic after flu and other debilitating illnesses.

Herbal Treatments

The plants our forefathers used to cure themselves are still around, their properties have not changed, they are still simple to grow and simple to use. They will promote our health and well-being and will rescue us from irritating small ailments.

ACNE
burdock, lady's mantle, nasturtium, parsley, soapwort and tansy

Treatment
A mild tea made from the herbs, fresh or dried is used as a facewash.

ANAEMIA
angelica, gentian, horsetail, nettle, thyme

Treatment
1. An infusion of 30 g/l oz angelica, nettle or thyme to 600 ml/1 pint boiling water taken in small cupfuls three times.

Warning
Gentian should only be taken under professional supervision. It should never be taken by pregnant women.

2. Horsetail
A decoction of 30g/1 oz dried herb to 600 ml/l pint water, soaked for 3 hours before boiling up. Take in wineglass doses three times a day.

APPETITE—LOSS OF
angelica, cardamom seeds, ginseng root, hop cones, mugwort, southernwood, tarragon, wormwood

Treatment
1. Use bought ginseng root and hop cones. Instructions for making tea comes with the packet.
2. Follow standard instructions for an infusion as for the other herbs.

ARTHRITIS
marjoram, meadowsweet

Treatment
Follow instructions for an infusion.

ARTERIOSCLEROSIS
chervil, couch grass roots, mistletoe.

Treatment
1. Follow instructions for an infusion.
2. Make a habit of taking a hot drink of milk poured over 2 crushed garlic cloves.
3. Soak a handful of mistletoe leaves in cold water for 12 hours and take wine-glassful doses three times a day.

Chervil

ASTHMA
evening primrose, maidenhair fern, plantain

Treatment
1. Follow instructions for an infusion.
2. Bought golden seal and lobelia. Follow instructions on the pack.
3. Smoke sage leaves instead of tobacco.

Golden seal

ATHLETE'S FOOT
garlic

Treatment
Rub a cut clove on the affected parts.

BAD BREATH
caraway seeds, vervain

Treatment
1. Chew caraway seeds after meals.
2. Vervain. Make a strong infusion and use as a mouthwash, especially if gums are infected.

BED WETTING
nettle seeds

Treatment
Take in a spoonful of honey before cleaning the teeth and going to bed.

BLADDER
golden rod, parsley

Treatment
Follow instructions for an infusion.

BLADDER GRAVEL
parsley piert, shepherd's purse, valerian

Treatment
Follow instructions for an infusion.

Parsley

BLOOD PRESSURE
High—foxglove, ginseng

Treatment
Use bought preparations.

Low—balm, shepherd's purse

Treatment
Follow instructions for an infusion.

Regulator—hawthorn

Treatment
Use flowers to make a standard infusion.

BOILS
Burdock, chamomile, fenugreek seeds, flax (linseed) seeds, nasturtium and sage

Treatment
1. A decoction of chopped leaves makes a good face wash.
2. 30 g/1 oz root, boiled in 600 ml/1 pint of water until reduced by a quarter, taken in wineglassful doses three times a day.
3. Chamomile flowers, fenugreek seeds, flax (linseed) seeds, nasturtium and sage leaves made into a poultice.

BOWELS
Inflamed—slippery elm

Treatment
Use an enema made from 30 g/1 oz powdered bark to 600 ml/1 pint water.

Laxative—borage, cowslip, horehound, nasturtium, violet.

Treatment
Follow instructions for an infusion. Chew a few mustard seeds.

Constant constipation—aloe, cascara, senna, chickweed, dandelion, golden rod, flax seeds

Treatment
1. Aloe (dried preparation of the gel), cascara (bought preparation), senna leaves and pods (bought preparation).
2. Chickweed, dandelion, golden rod. Follow instructions for an infusion.
3. Chew some flax seeds. Not suitable for pregnant women.

BRAIN
chervil, eyebright

Treatment
Follow instructions for an infusion.

Chickweed

BRONCHITIS
coltsfoot, flax (linseed), garlic, ginger, horehound, lime flowers, maidenhair fern, nasturtium, pennyroyal, sage, St. John's wort, slippery elm, thyme, verbena, vervain

Treatment
1. Follow instructions for an infusion.
2. Garlic
Crush a clove of garlic, add to a small jar vaseline and use as a chest rub.
3. Flax seeds
Soak 3 tsp of seeds in cold water for 2 hours. Strain and drink.

Garlic

BRUISES AND SPRAINS
Bruises: arnica, marigold (tincture)
Sprains: marjoram, St. John's wort (oil) comfrey, tansy and wormwood (tincture)

BURNS AND SCALDS
aloe (gel), comfrey (poultice), nettle (homeopathic preparation URTICA), plantain (cool poultice), St John's wort (oil)

CHILBLAINS
marigold flowers (poultice)

COLDS AND CHILLS
angelica, balm, catmint, chamomile, elderflowers, golden rod, meadowsweet, pennyroyal, St, John's wort, vervain, yarrow

Treatment
Follow instructions for an infusion.

COLITIS
lobelia, (under professional guidance), marshmallow (syrup), slippery elm powder mixed with water or milk taken as a drink

COUGHS
anise, borage, elecampane, horehound, hyssop, maidenhair fern, marshmallow, mullein, savory

Treatment
1. Follow instructions for an infusion.
2. Marigold (syrup)

CORNS
dandelion, fenugreek, garlic, marigold

Treatment
1. Marigold
Press crushed flowers against corn.
2. Bathe frequently in tea made from fenugreek seeds.

Marigold

CRAMP
cowslip, pennyroyal
Stomach cramp-catmint

Treatment
Follow instructions for an infusion.

CYSTITIS
horsetail, juniper berries, lovage, St. John's wort, shepherd's purse

Treatment
1. Follow instructions for an infusion.
2. Horsetail. Use a decoction.

DIARRHOEA
hawthorn berries, lime flowers, meadowsweet, mullein, periwinkle, shepherd's purse

Treatment
1. Follow instructions for an infusion.
2. Hawthorn berries
Follow instructions for a decoction.

DIGESTION
Aids to—angelica, anise, balm, caraway, centaury, dandelion, dill, elecampane, fennel, golden rod, horseradish root, juniper berries, marjoram, meadowsweet, mint, nettle, parsley, red clover, sage, salad burnet, slippery elm, verbena

Treatment
1. Follow instruction for an infusion.
2. Caraway seeds
Chew after a meal.
3. Slippery elm powder
Mix with milk and take small drink after meals.

DISINFECTANT
golden rod, lavender, rosemary, sage, thyme, wormwood

Treatment
Use as an infusion to bathe wounds.

DIURETIC
bay, dandelion, elderflowers, germander, horseradish, golden rod, groundsel, horehound, juniper berries. lady's bedstraw, mugwort, nasturtium, nettle, parsley, plantain, shallot, sorrel, woodruff

Treatment
1. Follow instructions for an infusion.
2. Decoctions of elecampane root and horsetail.
3. Pour 600 ml/1 pint boiling water over 30 g/1 oz of well-hammered horseradish root. Take 3 times a day in wineglassful doses.

EAR-ACHE
poppy seeds

Treatment
Follow instructions for an infusion.

ECZEMA
chickweed, golden rod

Treatment
Follow instructions for an infusion.

EMPHYSEMA
nasturtium leaves

Chickweed

Treatment
Follow instructions for an infusion.

EPILEPSY
mistletoe, skullcap, valerian

Treatment
1. Soak mistletoe leaves in cold water for 12 hours. Take in wineglassful doses three times a day.
2. Use infusions of skullcap or valerian.

EXPECTORANT
horehound, elecampane root, lobelia

Treatment
1. Use an infusion of horehound.
2. Use elecampane root to make a decoction.
3. Lobelia. Use a commercial preparation.

EYES
Sore: Centaury, chickweed, eyebright, fennel, golden rod, lovage, melilot, plantain, rue
Cataracts: Aconite, couch grass, fenugreek, garlic, hyssop, plantain, purslane

Treatment
Use a weak infusion as an eye-bath.

FEVER
aconite, couch grass, fenugreek seeds, hyssop, plantain

Treatment
Use a standard infusion.

1. Fenugreek seeds. 15 g/½ oz only
2. Hyssop flowers. 10 g/¼ oz only

FLATULENCE
angelica, cardamom seeds, catmint, centaury, juniper berries, lovage, melilot, tarragon, valerian

Treatment
Follow instructions for an infusion.

Angelica

GOUT
lime flowers, soapwort, male fern

Treatment
1. Lime flowers (infusion)
2. Male fern (poultice)
3. Soapwort root. Boil 30 g/1 oz of soapwort root in 300 ml/½ pint of water. Take 1 tablespoon 3 times a day.

HAY FEVER
Eyebright, mullein

Treatment
Use an infusion.

HEADACHE
Balm, lavender, rosemary, valerian, vervain

Treatment
1. Use an infusion.
2. Lavender. Rub oil on temples.

HEART
aconite (sedative), foxglove, hawthorn, lily-of-the-valley, motherwort, rosemary (palpitations), soapwort (angina)

Treatment
1. Aconite, foxglove, hawthorn, lily-of the-valley and soapwort should all be taken under professional supervision.
2. Motherwort and rosemary. Follow instructions for an infusion.

HAEMORRHAGE
golden rod, horsetail, nettle, periwinkle, plantain, shepherd's purse, yarrow

Treatment
1. Crushed leaves of yarrow applied to a wound will stop bleeding.
2. Horsetail. Apply fresh cut leaves, crushed leaves or a poultice of leaves to external bleeding. Take a decoction for internal bleeding.
3. Nettle. Nettle juice on cotton wool as a nasal plug will stop a nose-bleed.
4. Taking a decoction of shepherd's purse will stop a nose bleed.
5. Periwinkle. Taking a weak infusion will help to stop external and internal bleeding.
6. Yarrow in homeopathic doses is good for bleeding piles, unrelenting nose-bleeds and undue loss of blood after confinement or tooth extraction.

HICCUPS
dill, mint, wood betony

Treatment
Follow instructions for an infusion.

INSECT BITES
costmary, fennel, feverfew, gentian, hyssop, marigold, parsley, plantain, savory

Treatment
1. The leaves of costmary, hyssop, marigold, parsley, plantain or savory rubbed on a bite or sting will ease itching and pain.
2. Sprigs of fennel and feverfew about the person will keep insects away.

INSOMNIA
hawthorn, hops, lady's slipper, marjoram, melilot, mullein, valerian

Treatment
Take hawthorn flowers, hop cones, lady's slipper, marjoram, melilot, mullein or valerian in an infusion.

JAUNDICE
soapwort in homeopathic preparation.

KIDNEYS
Poor function—golden rod, lime flowers, lovage, parsley
Stones or gravel in—golden rod, lady's bedstraw, nettle, parsley piert, shepherd's purse, yarrow

Treatment
Follow instructions for an infusion.

LACTATION
To increase—anise, dill, fennel, fenugreek seeds
To dry up—sage

Treatment
Follow instructions for an infusion. Only use 15 g/½ oz of fenugreek seeds.

Fennel

LIVER
dandelion, golden rod, horehound, hyssop, lime flowers, marigold, rosemary, vervain, woodruff, wormwood, yarrow
fennel root, poke root (spleen)

Treatment
1. Follow instructions for an infusion.
2. Fennel root. Use a decoction.
3. Poke root. Use a bought preparation.

LUMBAGO
juniper, vervain

Treatment
Use poultices.

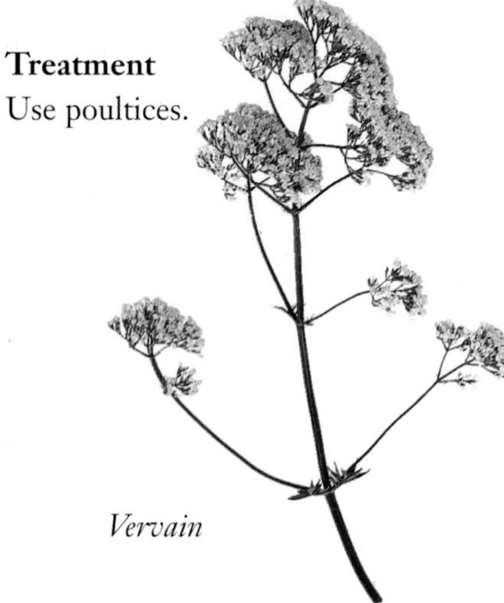
Vervain

LUNGS
chickweed, marshmallow, mullein, slippery elm

Treatment
1. Chickweed, mullein. Use infusions.
2. Marshmallow. Use a syrup.
3. Slippery elm. 1 to 3 tsp of powdered bark in hot milk as a drink.

MENOPAUSE
mugwort

Treatment
Follow instructions for an infusion.

MENSTRUAL DISORDERS
balm, chamomile, (premenstrual tension), costmary, germander, groundsel, hop cones, lady's mantle (excessive bleeding), melilot, motherwort, mugwort, nettle, parsley, pennyroyal, rue, shepherd's purse (excessive bleeding with pain), southernwood, valerian, vervain, yarrow

Treatment
1. Follow instructions for an infusion.
2. Pasque flowers in a bought homeopathic preparation for pre-menstrual tension.

MIGRAINE
fennel, fenugreek seeds (15 g/½ oz to 600 ml water/1 pint), pasque flower (15 g/½ oz to 600 ml water), thyme, valerian

Treatment
1. Follow instructions for an infusion.
2. Pasque flower in homeopathic preparation.

MUCUS
To rid the body of mucus waste eat finely-grated horseradish.

Suggestions
1. Brown bread sandwiches with plenty of butter, a touch of tarragon and plenty of grated horseradish root.
2. Grated beetroot mixed with grated horse-radish, well-seasoned in sweetened vinegar as a relish for meat and fish dishes.
3. Get into the habit of sneaking some into almost everything—bar sweet dishes or cakes etc. It livens any cooked vegetable, meat dish, home-made cheeses and mayonnaises.

Use horseradish sauce and horseradish butter frequently and, as soon as they are made.

Horseradish sauce
Add a little salt and a pinch or two of mustard to the very finely grated root and fold into some well-whipped cream.

Horseradish butter
Pound some very well-grated root into butter—the amount to suit one's taste. If it doesn't seem fine enough, push it through a sieve.

NAUSEA
pennyroyal

Treatment
Follow instructions for an infusion.

Pennyroyal

NERVES
Food for—red clover, sage
Exhaustion of—pennyroyal
Sedatives for—chamomile, cowslip, evening primrose, hop cones, lady's bedstraw, lady's slipper, lime flowers, mugwort, skullcap, valerian, verbena, vervain, wood betony

Treatment
Follow instructions for an infusion. Any ginseng preparation will stimulate nerves.

NEURALGIA
aconite, catmint, feverfew, vervain

Treatment
Follow instructions for an infusion.

NIGHTMARES
rosemary

Treatment
Follow instructions for an infusion.

Rosemary

PAIN RELIEF
elderflowers, hops, meadowsweet, melilot, valerian

Treatment
Follow instructions for an infusion.

PERSPIRATION
Bringing on—angelica, balm, elderflowers, germander, groundsel, juniper berries, lime flowers, marigold flowers, meadowsweet, pennyroyal, yarrow
Checking—myrtle

Treatment

1. To bring on perspiration follow instructions for an infusion of angelica, balm, elderflowers, germander, groundsel, juniper berries, lime flowers, marigold flowers, meadowsweet, pennyroyal or yarrow.
2. Powdered ginger in hot water sweetened with honey will bring on perspiration.
3. Powdered mustard in a hot bath will bring on perspiration.
4. Follow instructions for an infusion of myrtle leaves to check perspiration.

PILES

cascara sagrada, catmint, elder, plantain, Solomon's seal. witchhazel

Treatment

1. Cascara sagrada. Drinking a weak tea will ease the irritation.
2. Catmint elder leaves, plantain. Use to make a wash for local application.
3. Solomon's seal. Powdered as a poultice for inflamed piles.
4. Witch-hazel in a decoction as an enema for bleeding piles.

Some decoction added to vaseline makes a soothing ointment which will shrink the piles.

SINUS

elderflowers, horseradish, rosemary

Treatment

1. Follow instructions for infusions of elderflowers and rosemary.
2. Horseradish in a bought preparation.

Horseradish

SKIN

burdock, chickweed, golden rod (eczema and psoriasis), poke root

Treatment

1. Burdock, chickweed and golden rod. Follow instructions for an infusion.
2. Use a decoction of poke root.as an external wash for eczema and impetigo.

SORE THROAT

bergamot, sage, thyme

Treatment

Follow instructions for an infusion.

Thyme

STIMULANT

caraway, germander; ginger, horseradish, hyssop, marjoram, nettle, rosemary, southernwood

Treatment

Follow instructions for infusions of caraway leaves, germander, (sage-leaved variety), hyssop, marjoram, nettle, rosemary and southernwood.

SUNBURN

1. Apply aloe gel to sore places.
2. Use an infusion salad burnet to bathe the skin.

TONIC

angelica root, agrimony, borage, chervil, chickweed, costmary, dandelion, eyebright, fenugreek seeds (15 g/l oz) germander, hop cones, horehound, lady's slipper, marjoram, motherwort, mugwort, nettle, rosemary, salad burnet, sorrel, southernwood, sweet cicely, thyme, woodruff, wormwood

Treatment

Follow instructions for an infusion.

TONSILLITIS

fenugreek, sage

Treatment

1. Add 15 g of fenugreek to 600 ml/l pint boiling water as a drink and a gargle.
2. Use sage tea as a drink and a gargle.

TOOTHACHE

marjoram, mint, poppyseed

Treatment

Follow instructions for an infusion.

ULCERS

chickweed, golden rod, golden seal, marigold, St. John's wort, vervain

Treatment

Follow instructions for an infusion and use it to bathe the ulcers.

URINATION

Cleansing—parsley-piert, uva-ursi
Painful—St. John's wort
Suppressed—catmint, juniper berries, ladies' bedstraw, rosemary

Parsley

Treatment

Follow instructions for an infusion.

VAGINAL PROBLEMS

golden rod, lady's mantle, uva-ursi, lavender

Treatment

1. Use a weak infusion of lavender as a douche for leucorrhea.
2. Golden rod, lady's mantle, uva-ursi. Follow instructions for an infusion.

VARICOSE VEINS

To strengthen veins—melilot
Ulcerated—agrimony, marigold, yarrow

Treatment

1. Take a melilot infusion regularly.
2. Follow instructions for an infusion of agrimony, marigold or yarrow and use as a soothing wash.

VOMITING

To induce—mustard
To reduce—mint

Treatment

1. Mustard powder dissolved in hot water and taken as a drink.
2. Follow instructions to make an infusion of mint.

WARTS

dandelion, greater celandine

Treatment

Apply juice to the warts night and morning.

WHOOPING COUGH

evening primrose, lobelia, mistletoe, pennyroyal, violet

Treatment

1. Using evening primrose or pennyroyal. follow the instructions for infusions.
2. Take violet. as a syrup.
3. Take lobelia and mistletoe under professional supervision.

WORMS

Expulsion of—horehound, hyssop, male fern, mugwort, nettle, plantain, rue, senna, southernwood, vervain, wormwood

Treatment

Follow instructions for an infusion.

WOUNDS

agrimony, golden rod, lady's mantle, marigold flowers, meadowsweet, parsley, rosemary, slippery elm, thyme, vervain, yarrow

Slow to heal—German chamomile, solomon's seal, yarrow

Treatment

1. Follow standard instructions for an infusion and use to bathe the wounds.
2. Mix some slippery elm powder with hot water and spread on lint or muslin and apply to septic wounds.
3. Use crushed yarrow poultice on wounds.

COMPOSITE HERB TREATMENTS

By taking a mixture of herbs an illness can be tackled on several fronts at the same time and, since some herbs act as a catalyst on others, efficacy is increased. A qualified herbalist will give more detailed advice than can be given here and should be consulted whenever a condition becomes really troublesome. The following recipes should be treated as recipes, not specifics.

If you don't have all the herbs needed just use as many as you have. It is a good idea to make up mixtures and store them, labelled, against the time they might be needed.

Herbal remedies work slowly. The use of drugs has taught us to expect quick results but many of us have found that they come at a price.

Acute diseases should, of course, be referred to a doctor without delay but for milder, non-threatening complaints, herbal medicine can be a satisfactory answer.

ARTHRITIS

1. mix equal quantities couch grass, meadowsweet and marjoram
2. add a half quantity coltsfoot
3. make an infusion and take in small cupful doses three times a day

OR

Use equal quantity elder leaves, golden rod and rosemary and a half quantity coltsfoot.

ASTHMA

Coltsfoot, comfrey, fennel seed, mistletoe, mullein, yarrow all contain potassium which sufferers from asthma and hay fever are said to lack. Tea made from one herb or a combination of some of them can help to make good the shortage.

BLOOD PRESSURE (HIGH)

Use catmint skullcap, mint or valerian tea.

BRONCHITIS

Make a decoction of red clover flowers and flax seeds.

Add honey and lemon to the tea and drink while hot.

COLDS

Take tea of either mint, yarrow, elderflower or mint.

CONSTIPATION

1. mix equal quantities mint, marjoram and senna leaves
2. add some chamomile flowers and make an infusion

ECZEMA

Make a tea from a mixture of equal quantities of violet leaves and senna pods, some meadowsweet and a few juniper berries.

OR

Use as a tea or a lotion mixture of equal quantities of chamomile, marigold flowers, sage, marshmallow and vervain.

HEADACHE

Tea made from a mixture of equal quantities of catmint, mint and valerian

OR

a tea of chamomile flowers and mint leaves. OR

a tea of feverfew, ground ivy, rosemary and wood betony.

HICCUPS

Slowly sip tea made from mint and wood betony.

INSOMNIA

Balm and marjoram with a lesser quantity anise and valerian as a nightcap tea.

OR

equal quantities hops, skullcap and valerian.

OR

mint with half the quantity of rue and wood betony sweetened with honey to improve the taste.

KIDNEYS

Tea made from equal quantities chamomile flowers, dandelion, juniper berries, parsley and uva-ursi.

LACTATION—TO INCREASE

Tea made from equal quantities of basil, fennel, nettle and vervain.

LIVER

Tea made from equal quantities of angelica, chamomile flowers, dandelion, gentian, golden rod, horsetail and parsley. If you can't get all the ingredients use as many as you can.

LUNGS

Tea made from equal quantities of marshmallow, chickweed and mullein.

MENSTRUAL DIFFICULTIES

Tea made from equal quantities of chamomile flowers, mugwort, rosemary, sage and shepherd's purse.

MIGRAINE

Fenugreek and thyme tea.

NERVES

Tea made from equal quantities of valerian and mint with a few chamomile and lavender flowers. OR from mint leaves with the addition of some anise, hops, horsetail and chamomile flowers.

PAIN

Severe continuing pain should be referred to a doctor. In the meantime a tea made from equal quantities of balm, elder flowers, lavender flowers, hawthorn leaves and St. John's wort could give some relief.

VOMITING

Only for simple cases—severe ones should be referred to a doctor. Tea made from equal quantities of balm, chamomile flowers, centaury, mint and fennel seed.

WATER—EXCESS IN THE BODY

Tea made from equal quantities of juniper berries, horsetail, nettle, rosemary and yarrow.

Essential
Oils &
Aromatics

Essential oils are the concentrated vital essences of aromatic plants. They contain therapeutic properties and are used in perfumes, cosmetics and aromatheraphy—a system of healing the body through massage, inhalation or bathing with blended essential oils.

The oils are found in glands in one or more parts of the plant. For example in basil it is found in the leaves, in roses in the flowers, in oranges in the fruit and in sandalwood in the wood and so on. In nature, heat causes the essences to evaporate and protect the plant from bacteria, extremes in temperature and other threats to its health and wellbeing.

The essential oil of herbs should not be confused with oil obtained by leaving herbs soaking in a bottle of oil in the warm for several days or by oil extracted by heat. It is something quite different and beyond the ability of most people to create for themselves.

The methods used to extract the oil are time consuming and expensive, requiring a high degree of know-how and when you realise that it takes over a hundred kilos of rose petals to produce 4 or 5 teaspoonsful of oil it is clear that this is something best left to professionals.

Essential oil is expensive—given the time and effort needed to produce it one could not expect otherwise. If you find cheaper synthetic oils on the market resist the temptation to buy—they simply do not have the healing power of the natural ones.

Essential oils are only used a few drops at a time and will last for years if stored in small brown or dark green well-sealed bottle in a cool dark place.

They should not be used undiluted unless an aromatherapist says so.

They should not be used during pregnancy unless a professional aromatherapist says it is safe to do so.

They should never be taken orally unless under the guidance of a professional aromatherapist.

If taking drugs for a medical condition consult a professional aromatherapist before undertaking treatment with essential oils.

All essential oils must be kept away from the eyes and from naked flames.

OILS

Oils are described as having a top, middle or base note according to the rate at which they evaporate.

Top notes

These are the most stimulating and uplifting oils. They are strongly and bracingly scented but the perfume does not hold for very long; 3-24 hours.

Top note oils: basil, bergamot, clary sage, coriander, eucalyptus, lemongrass, neroli, peppermint, sage and thyme

Middle notes

The middle notes are moderately volatile, lasting 2-3 days, and affect the metabolism and body functions. They have a less strong perfume.

Middle note oils: balm, chamomile, fennel, geranium, hyssop, juniper, lavender, rosemary

Base notes

These are the slowest to evaporate. Their sweet, soothing scent can last for as much as a week. They are the most soothing and relaxing of the oils.

A mixture of all three types is a sensible choice when considering treatment.

Base note oils: cedarwood, clove, frankincense, ginger, jasmine, rose, sandalwood

Bottles of essential oils are best stored in containers away from the light.

AROMATHERAPY

Aromatherapy is the art of using the perfumed essential oils of plants to treat sickness of the body and mind and to stimulate the body so that it can resist illness. The oils can be inhaled—there are some very attractive oil burners on the market, added to the bath water, massaged into the skin or used in a compress.

We all know the pleasure a scented garden gives—how one drinks in the perfume and relaxes with a smiling sigh. The perfume passes over the nerve cells in the nasal passage and a message is sent directly to the brain. The transmission is more direct than the one made by stimulation of the eye or ear. The message passes along a pathway of nerves to the hypothalamus which controls the workings of the endocrinal glands and then to the thalamus which is a conduit to the conscious activity of the brain. The release of hormones which act upon the body in many different ways can be triggered by a simple scent.

The potency of fragrance has been known throughout history but it is only in comparatively recent times that sufficient research has been made to enable accurate analyses of the properties carried by the different essential oils.

THE AROMABATH

Close bathroom door and windows and run a warm bath. When the water has settled add up to 10 drops essential oil and move it around. It is volatile and the scent will rise and mingle with the steam. Soak in the bath, stroking the oil over your body and inhale the steam.

Relaxing and calming bath
2 drops lavender
2 drops bergamot
2 drops cedarwood

Relaxing and meditative bath
6 drops frankincense
4 drops patchouli
2 drops bergamot

Relieving nervousness bath
6 drops geranium
4 drops basil

Bath for the worn-out
4 drops lavender
2 drops geranium
2 drops neroli

Warnings

- *Do not use cedarwood or juniper during pregnancy*
- *Do not use fennel or hyssop for epileptic sufferers*
- *Use clary sage and sage in moderation*

Relaxing muscles bath
4 drops rosemary
2 drops marjoram
3 drops lavender

Bath for insomnia
4 drops chamomile
2 drops lavender
4 drops neroli
2 drops marjoram

Pick-me-up bath
3 drops rosemary
2 drops lemon
2 drops frankincense

CARRIER OILS

As essential oils are highly concentrated they are used by the drop and must be diluted in a carrier oil for skin application.

Almond oil
Almond oil is a good skin oil on its own. and is a favourite "carrier" as it is very smooth, has little smell, is rich in protein and keeps well.

Apricot kernel oil
Apricot kernel oil is light and contains vitamin A and some fatty acids. Good for the face particularly if the skin is dry, or ageing.

Avocado oil
Avocado oil is also rich in nutrients but is heavier.

Jojoba oil
Jojoba oil is light, rich in vitamin E, gives a satin feel to the skin and keeps well.

Grapeseed, soya and sunflower oil
Grapeseed, soya and sunflower oil are all good.

Hazelnut oil
Hazelnut penetrates the most easily and deeply and nourishes the skin.

Olive oil and sesame oil
Olive oil and sesame oil can be used at a pinch but they have a strong scent and taste of their own.

ESSENTIAL EFFECTS OF OILS

Basil *uplifting, refreshing, clarifying, aids concentration*
Bergamot *refreshing, uplifting*
Chamomile *refreshing, relaxing, calming, soothing, balancing*
Cedarwood *sedating, calming, soothing, strengthening*
Clary sage *warming, relaxing, uplifting, calming, euphoric*
Cypress *relaxing, refreshing, astringent*
Eucalyptus *head clearing, antiseptic, decongestant, invigorating*
Fennel *carminative, eases wind and indigestion*
Frankincense *relaxing, rejuvenating, eases breathing, dispels fears*
Geranium *refreshing, relaxing, balancing, harmonising*
Hyssop *decongestant*
Jasmine *relaxing, soothing, confidence building*
Juniper *refreshing, stimulating, relaxing, diuretic*
Lavender *refreshing, relaxing, therapeutic, calming, soothing*
Lemon *refreshing, stimulating, uplifting, motivating*
Lemongrass *toning, refreshing, fortifying*
Marjoram *warming, fortifying, sedating*
Melissa *uplifting, refreshing*
Myrrh *toning, strengthening, rejuvenating*
Neroli *relaxing, dispels fears*
Orange *refreshing, relaxing*
Peppermint *cooling, refreshing, head clearing*
Pine *refreshing, antiseptic, invigorating, stimulating*
Rose *relaxing, soothing, sensual, confidence building*
Rosemary *invigorating, refreshing, stimulating, clarifying*
Sandalwood *relaxing, warming, confidence building, grounding*
Tea Tree *antiseptic, refreshing, strengthens to immune system*
Thyme *antiseptic, refreshing, strengthens to immune system*
Ylang ylang *relaxing, soothing, enhances sensuality*

ESSENTIAL OILS IN MASSAGE

Essential oils have to be used diluted for application to the skin.

The oil chosen to be the "carrier" should be pure, have no scent, be cold-pressed so that the properties remain intact, not be sticky but have a texture which enables the hands to move easily over the skin.

Most people make a mix and keep the bottle ready for use. Don't make more than can be used in under 10 to12 weeks as although the essential oil does not go off, the carrier oil will and the smell becomes unattractive. Do not leave the bottle unsealed for any length of time—air accelerates deterioration.

When making the mixture the amount of essential oil used is not great—about 30 drops to a 600 ml/1 pint bottle of carrier oil. Don't be tempted to use more, particularly if there are any emotional problems involved in the condition being treated. It is better to make small amounts at a time and use them at one treatment. than to make a big bottle and have it standing about. The amount of oil needed for a full body massage is not great—certainly no more than the amount of milk used in a cup of Indian tea.

BASIC MASSAGE STROKES

STROKING

Most aromatherapy massage is made up of a long stroking movement called effleurage. The movements are rhythmic and flowing and they are the ones you use the most. You use them when applying oil and to link other movements. You can do a whole body massage using only stroking movements.

By changing the speed and pressure you can change the effect of the massage. Slow movements, for example are calming, while fast movements will stimulate.

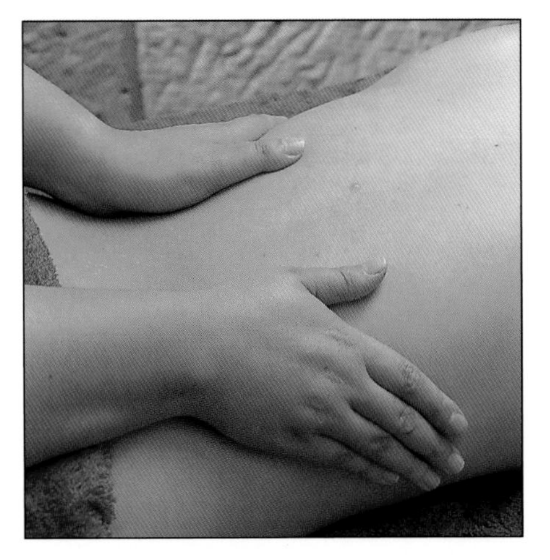

1 Start with your hands side by side and glide them slowly upwards, leading with your fingers. Lean on your hands exerting a steady pressure through your palms and the heel of the hands.

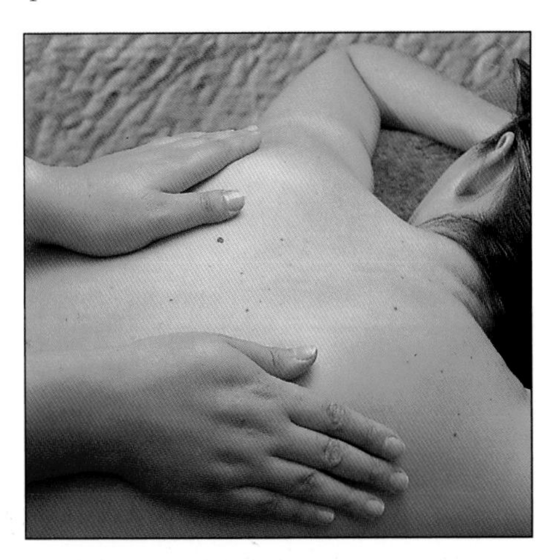

2 As you reach the top of the back, fan your hands out making a light, relaxed return stroke. The hands must be moulded to the shape of the body.

TOP NOTE OIL BLENDS

Head, the digestion and the lungs	*Basil with balm, bergamot, geranium, hyssop, marjoram, and lavender.*
Depression, the skin, and digestion	*Bergamot with chamomile, coriander, jasmine, rose and sandalwood.*
Depression, bad digestion, insomnia, menstrual difficulties	*Clary sage with bergamot, cedar wood, geranium, juniper, lavender and sandalwood.*
Nervous debility, bad digestion	*Coriander with bergamot and neroli.*
Colds and viruses and chest problems	*Eucalyptus with balm, hyssop, lavender and lemon grass.*
Acne, sagging skin and the digestion	*Lemongrass with basil, geranium and lavender.*
Bad digestion, travel sickness and headache	*Peppermint with balm and marjoram.*
Skin, chest, will kill germs	*Sage with balm, bergamot, hyssop, peppermint and rosemary.*
Depression headaches, "chests" and warding off germs	*Thyme with balm, bergamot and rosemary.*

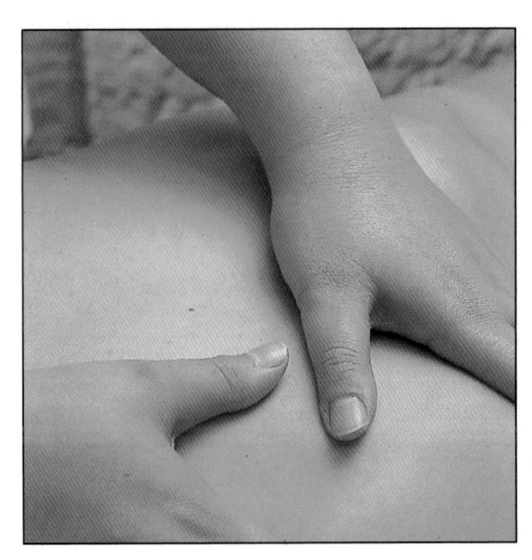

Thumb stroking: For small areas such as legs, use your thumbs to stroke firmly upwards and out to the side, one thumb first then the other moving a little higher up before moving ou

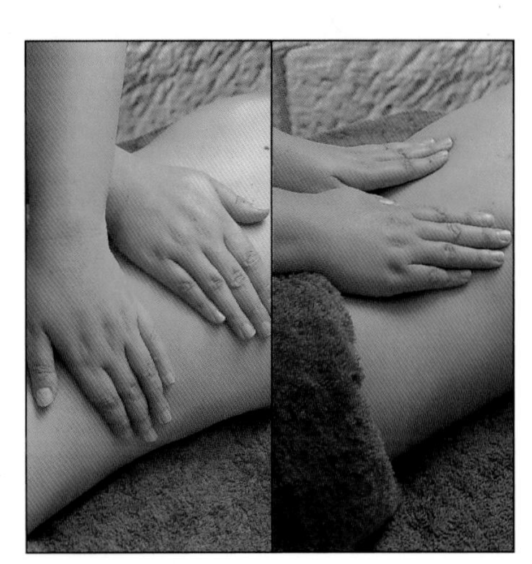

Circling: Put the hands in the same position as for stroking, but move them in circles – one clockwise and the other anti-clockwise.

KNEADING - PETRISSAGE

This is like kneading dough and is used on the fleshy areas such as hips and thighs. It stretches and relaxes tense muscles, improves the circulation and helps reduce fatigue.

Light kneading affects the skin and top layer of muscles.

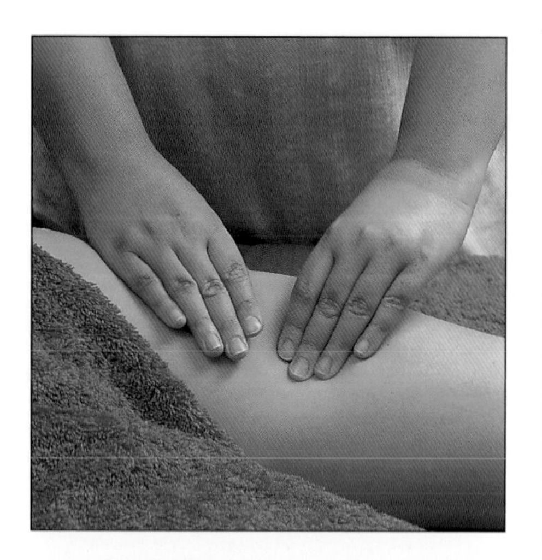

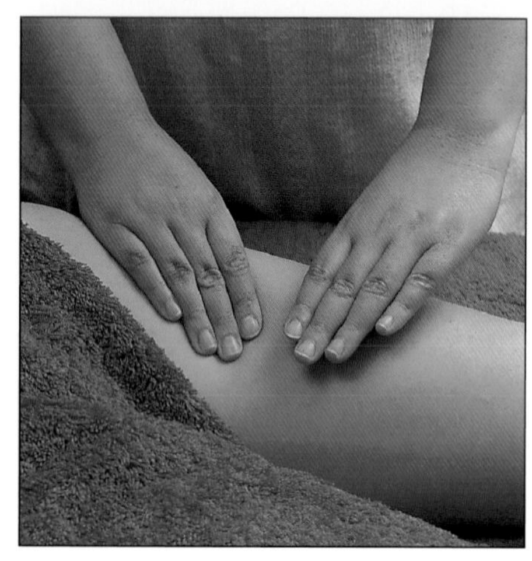

Pick up a handful of flesh and squeeze or roll it with one hand, then the other. Pick up the adjacent skin and repeat to make a rippling movement as if you were kneading dough.

THE DO'S AND DON'TS OF MASSAGE

- *Spread the oil across the skin with smooth strokes before you start the massage.*
- *Always warm your hands and the oil before you start.*
- *Never put heavy downward pressure on bony areas or organs.*

MIDDLE NOTE OIL BLENDS

The relief of tension and depression and painful menstruation	*Balm with geranium and juniper*
A gentle relaxant, relieving pain and insomnia	*Chamomile with bergamot, geranium, lavender, marjoram and rose*
Easing the digestion and clearing excess water from the body and for oily skin	*Fennel with geranium, lavender, rose and sandalwood*
Liver, kidneys, skin and the female reproductive organs	*Geranium will mix with all oils*
For anxieties, the circulation, the chest and the stomach	*Hyssop with clary sage, lavender, rosemary and sage*
For the skin, aching muscles and depression	*Juniper with bergamot, geranium, lavender, rosemary and sandalwood*
For insomnia, headaches, indigestion and poor skin	*Lavender is good with most oils*
For tension, chills, muscular cramps and poor digestion	*Marjoram with bergamot, chamomile, lavender and rosemary*
For tiredness, headaches, muscular pains, poor circulation	*Rosemary with basil, lavender and peppermint*

RAKING

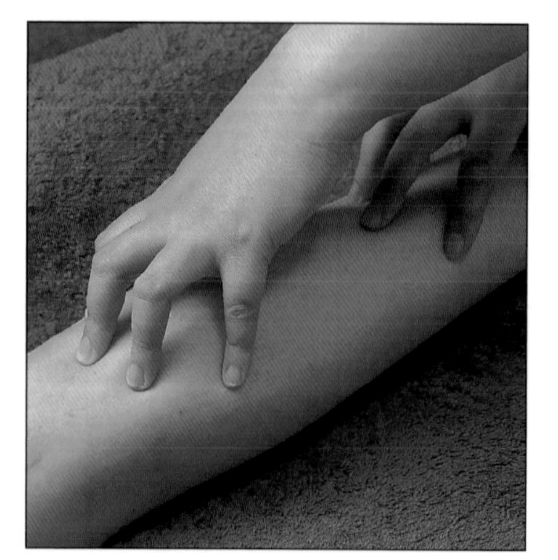

Imagine that your finger tips are the end of a rake – keep them bent at the joints, but stiff. Make firm, pulling movements back towards you. You can either use both hands at the same time or one after the other.

FRICTION RUB

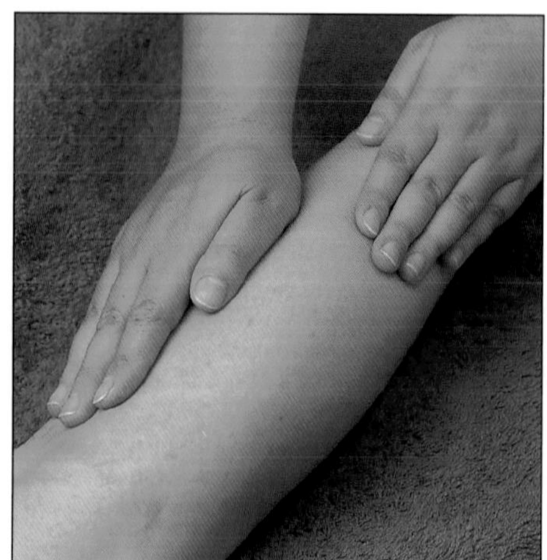

Place your palms down and your hands flat. Move one hand up and the other hand down, in fast, short, sawing movements.

PRESSURES

Tension is relieved by exerting deep, direct pressure on the muscles either side of the spine and around the shoulder area. It is also very relaxing.

Apply the pressure gradually and never poke sharply. Do not use a lot of oil or your hands will slip around.

Static pressure: *Place the fingers on the skin either side of the spine and gradually lean on them. Press for a few seconds, release and glide to the next point.*

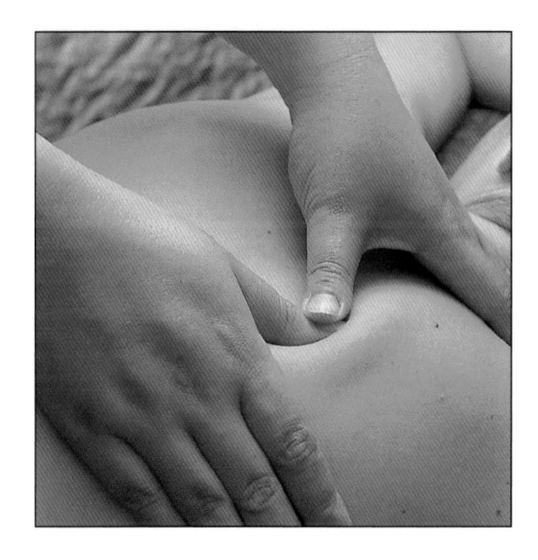

Circular pressure: *Press as for static pressure and then make small, deep circular movements, circling the skin against the underlying muscle.*

BASE NOTE OIL BLENDS

For anxiety, cystitis and the lungs	*Cedarwood is good with bergamot, juniper and rosemary*
For warming the body and enlivening the skin	*Frankincense will blend with most oils*
For stress, headaches, poor skin and circulation	*Rose blends with most oils*

FACIAL MASSAGE STROKES

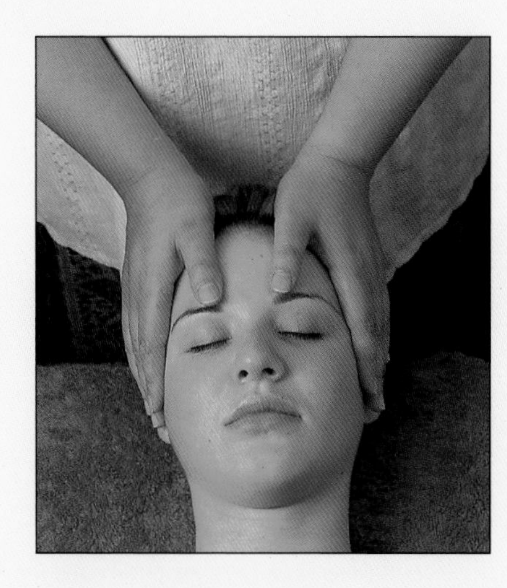

Stroke out from the centre of the forehead to ease tension.

Lightly stroke the neck upwards and along the jawline to the ears.

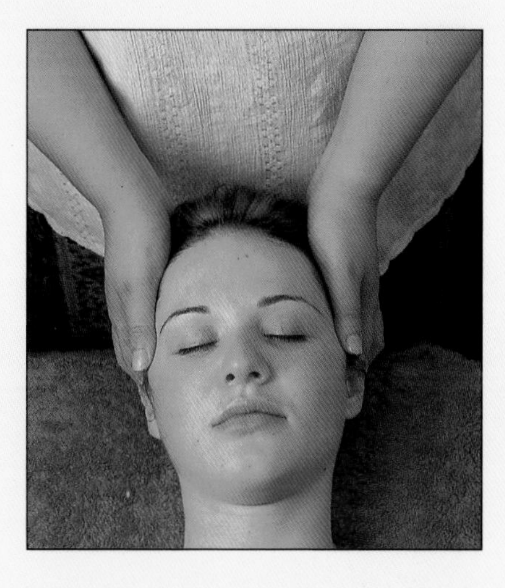

Move your fingers from the centre of the forehead out towards, and along, the hairline.

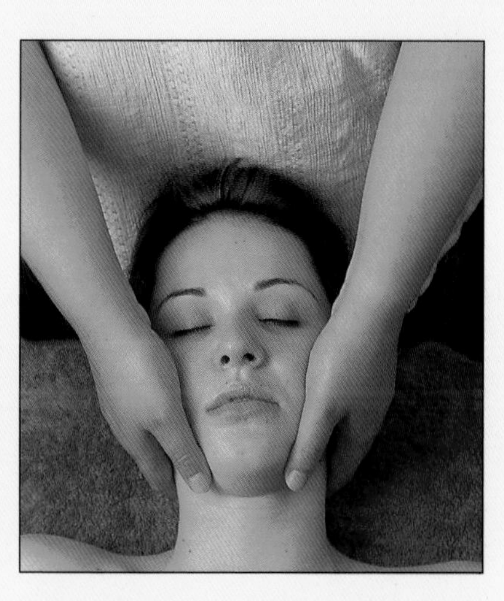

From the chin draw your thumbs along the jawbone up towards the ears.

BACK MASSAGE

Almost nothing is more relaxing than a back and shoulder massage – all the tension of the day quickly dissipates.

There are four basic movements: stroking (using the whole hand), kneading (rhythmic squeezing), friction (using the thumbs or balls of the thumbs) and feathering (light fingertip stroking).

From the Head

1 *Positioned at the head, gently place warm, oiled hands horizontally on either side of the spine on the top-most part of the back, fingers pointing towards the spine.*
2 *Use a sliding stroke, moving the hands down the length of the spine to the buttocks.*
3 *Fan out to the sides and lightly stroke up the sides to the armpits.*

From the Bottom

1 *Place hands at the base of the back, on either side of the spine, fingers close together and pointing towards the head.*
2 *Leaning into the strokes, slide hands up the back to the head.*
3 *Fan hands out across the shoulders and lightly stroke them down the sides to the starting point. Repeat.*

Other strokes

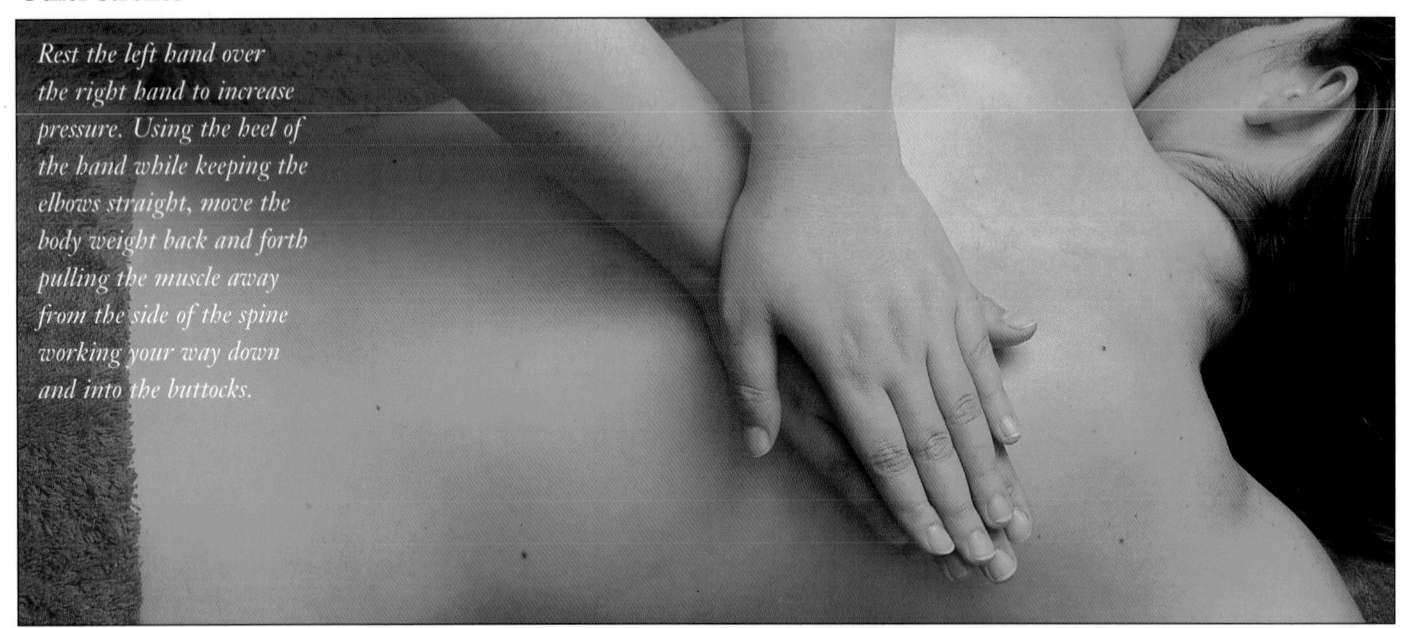

Rest the left hand over the right hand to increase pressure. Using the heel of the hand while keeping the elbows straight, move the body weight back and forth pulling the muscle away from the side of the spine working your way down and into the buttocks.

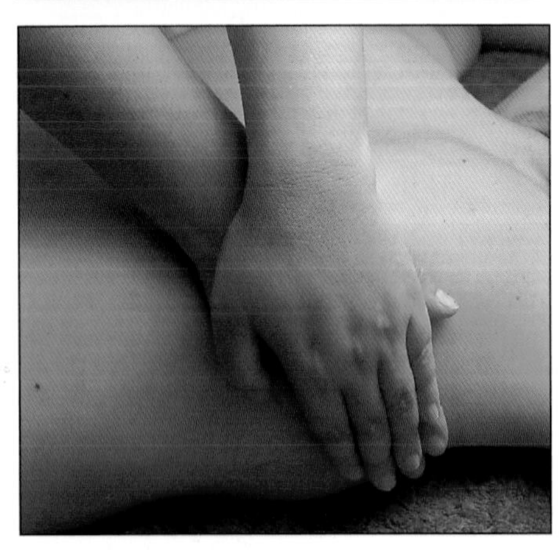

With the left hand resting over the right to increase the pressure, work in small circular movements from the base of the neck out and around the shoulder blades to release tension in the muscles.

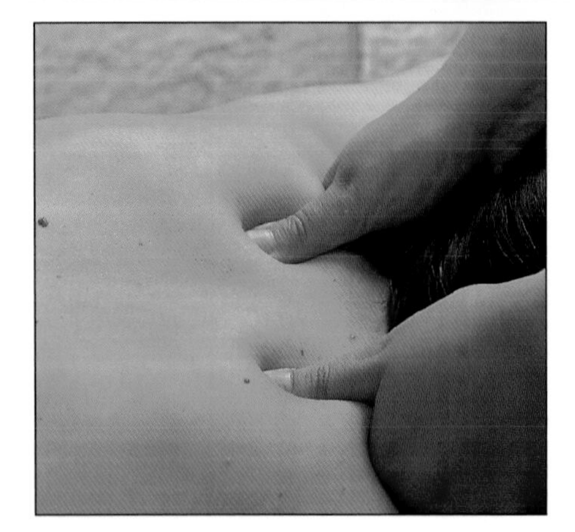

Starting at the base of the neck, place thumbs on either side of the spine. Apply firm circular pressure to small muscles at the top of the shoulders and around the shoulder blades. This same movement can be applied down either side of the spine to the lower back.

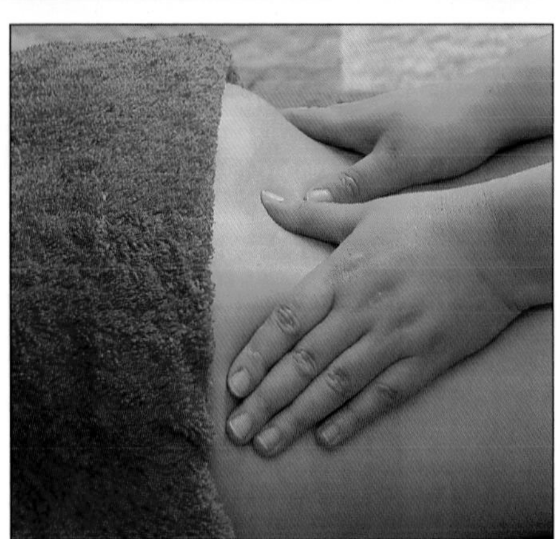

Apply circular pressures with thumbs around the bony triangle at the base of the spine.

USING OIL IN A SICK ROOM

Add a few drops of eucalyptus, sandalwood, pine, thyme or rosemary essential oil to the water in a fragrant oil burner, light the candle and let it burn until it is used up. Sit quietly and breathe deeply.

FOR INSOMNIA

Put one drop lavender or juniper essential oil on the pillow. If depressed as well as sleepless use clary sage instead.

COMPRESSES

Cooling compress

When a headache is troublesome or you have just sprained an ankle, make a cold compress by wringing out a soft cloth in cold water into which you have put 5-7 drops of lavender oil.

Hot compress

Check to see which oil is needed for your particular trouble and soak a cloth in hot water to which you have added 6 drops of oil. Wring out cloth, apply to affected spot, cover with a plastic bag and then wrap with a thick warm towel to keep in the heat.

STEAM INHALATION

(not suitable for asthmatics)

Put a few drops of essential oil into a bowl of very hot water and lean over it, keeping the face about a handspan above the water. Drape a towel over your head and the bowl and breathe in deeply through the nose.

After 5 to 10 minutes remove towel and wipe the face. The bowl of hot water can be left to continue releasing healing steam into the air.

If there is no time for a steam bath sprinkle a few drops of oil on to a tissue, hold it to the nose and take several deep breaths. Tuck the tissue into the front of your dress or place on the chest just behind the second shirt button down from the collar and go about your day.

OILS FOR SPECIFIC AILMENTS

A few drops of each one, used alone or mixed, can be added to some carrier oil and used in massage.

Arthritis—the temporary relief of pain: juniper, rosemary and thyme

Bronchitis—easing a cough: cedarwood, lavender, eucalyptus, pine, sandalwood

Bruises: arnica, fennel, geranium

Catarrh: cedarwood, frankincense, ginger, lavender, peppermint, sandalwood, thyme

Colds and flu: anise, basil, juniper, lavender, peppermint, thyme

Eczema—dry: chamomile, geranium, lavender, marigold
—weeping: bergamot, juniper, marigold

Headaches—temporary relief: chamomile, lavender

Insomnia: basil, chamomile, lavender, neroli, sandalwood

Menstrual pain: chamomile, clary sage, jasmine

Muscular aches—temporary relief: anise, clary sage, ginger, lavender, lemongrass, marjoram, rosemary

Muscular cramp: basil, marjoram

CHANGING MOOD

Use these blends in vapourisers, baths or mixed in carrier oils for massages.

Good mood: *5 drops geranium, 4 drops frankinsence, 2 drops orange, 2 drops jasmine*

Balancing: *4 drops geranium, 3 drops neroli, 3 drops rose*

Restorative: *4 drops clary sage, 3 drops rose or lavender*

Uplifting: *5 drops bergamot, 5 drops clary sage*

ESSENTIAL OIL ROOM PERFUME BLENDS

Essential oil blends can be added to water-filled vapourisers, humidifiers, the molten wax of a candle or the dish of a diffuser.

Dreamtime: 2 drops each of chamomile, lavender, neroli

Enchantment: 2 drops each of geranium, orange, ylang ylang

Spicy: 4 drops bergamot, 1 drop each of cardamon and clove

Embrace: 2 drops each of bergamot, jasmine, sandalwood

Fresh: 1 drop cedarwood, 3 drops pine, 2 drops rosemary

Herbs in the Kitchen

Fresh herbs are not obtainable all the year round so we have to resort to dried or frozen ones.

The flavour of dried herbs depends on how well they have been picked and stored, how long kept and in what conditions, and whether used finely powdered or loosely crumbled. It will be considerably stronger than that of fresh ones because the oils become concentrated when herbs are dried.

Home-dried herbs are usually preferable to bought ones which are often sold in clear glass bottles or clear cellophane bags. You can see what you are getting and can reject them if the colour is less than fresh, but herbs keep better in the dark and who is to say how long they have been waiting to be bought? When you buy dried herbs—and most of us do at some time or another—always take the least amount possible and use it as quickly as possible.

Some herbs do not dry as successfully as others; their taste seems to change in the drying process; chervil, chives, salad burnet, some of the mints, and tarragon, for example, but fortunately they keep well in the freezer. The volatile oil they contain prevents them from losing either colour or flavour during freezing. Wrapped in foil, waxed paper or plastic or sealed in a butter carton they keep fresh for a surprisingly long time.

It is a waste of time to chop herbs before freezing them—the cuts produce oxidisation and they are so easy to chop in their frozen state.

The herbs won't do for garnishing when they defrost as they become limp, but the flavour and colour is unimpaired.

HERB COMBINATIONS

Few herbs actually swear at each other from a flavour point of view and there is scope for experimentation and personal choice but it is as well to know which herbs go best with sweet dishes and which with savoury ones. Sweet herbs would do nothing for a greasy meat dish.

If you dry your own herbs you can store them separately and use a little of each chosen one when cooking, but you can make a mix you like and store that.

Fish dishes: Chives, dill and parsley or basil, fennel, marjoram and thyme.

Chicken stuffing: Chives, lovage, marjoram and a few juniper berries or basil; chives, lovage, parsley, thyme or sage; chives and grated lemon peel.

Egg and cheese dishes: Chives, parsley, dill, lovage, tarragon.

Lamb and veal dishes: Marjoram, rosemary and summer savory.

Fried, roasted and barbecued meat: Chives, parsley, tarragon and thyme.

Pork dishes: Sage and basil.

TIPS FOR STORING AND BLENDING HERBS

- *Half a teaspoon of finely powdered herbs equals 2 teaspoons of crumbled herbs and 4-5 fresh, chopped ones.*

- *If you make a blend of herbs and keep it ready for use, store it in a dark glass, well-stoppered bottle and even though it is well sealed, don't keep it too long before using it. Herbs that have been stored for a long time can keep their flavour but somehow the life seems to have gone out often.*

- *If you hang herbs for drying in the kitchen, use them or store them as soon as you can for light, air and heat soon rob them of their flavour.*

- *Incidently, when using a blend of herbs don't use two strong ones together as the flavours will fight.*

Green beans: dill, marjoram, sage, summer savory.

Beetroot: basil, caraway, coriander, fennel.

Cabbage: caraway, fennel, lovage, mint.

Carrots: basil, mint, parsley, thyme.

Onions: sage, tarragon, thyme.

Peas: mint, tarragon.

Potatoes: basil, chives, fennel, fenugreek, mint, parsley, rosemary, sage.

Spinach: marjoram, mint.

Tomatoes: basil, marjoram, sage.

HERB MIXTURES FOR FLAVOURING FOOD

The blending of several different herbs which complement each other can turn an ordinary meal into a memorable one.

BOUQUETS GARNIS

This well-known flavouring is made by tying together a bundle of fresh or dried herbs; with a length of cotton and letting it dangle in the pot while the food is cooking. Alternately you can tie up the herbs in a piece of muslin and let it cook with the food and fish it out when cooking is over.

The classic bouquet garni for soup, fish or meat dishes

6 sprigs parsley
3 sprigs thyme and a bay leaf

Or if you use dried herbs:
1 tbsp parsley
1 tbsp tarragon
1 tsp rosemary
1 tsp thyme and a bayleaf

The blend of fresh herbs used by the French and known as "fines herbes" is a mild one. The herbs used are parsley, chervil and chives.

Opposite: *Chicken with herbal stuffing.*

Below: *Always use fresh organic produce.*

A QUICK GUIDE TO HERB FLAVOURS

Balm *especially lemon balm, has a clean, lemony taste*
Basil *is clovey and peppery*
Bergamot *is clean and sharp*
Borage and burnet *taste like cucumber*
Caraway *is spicy*
Coriander *has a scent and flavour all its own—it can be an acquired taste*
Dill *is aniseedy*
Fennel *is aniseedy*
Garlic *tastes like garlic*
Lovage *is yeasty and a bit like celery*
Marjoram *has a sweet, tangy taste*
Mint *can taste of peppermint, apple, pineapple, orange*
Nasturtium *leaves are peppery*
Oregano *is strong and tangy*
Parsley *has its own pleasant flavour*
Pennyroyal *has a strong, mint taste*
Rosemary *has a strong, dry taste*
Sage *is pleasant and pungent*
Sorrel *tastes sharp, lemony and rather bitter*
Summer savory *is like thyme but sweeter and milder*
Sweet cicely *has a taste between aniseed and liquorice*
Tarragon *tastes like sweet aniseed*
Thyme *is tangy*
Verbena *tastes lemony*
Vervain *is bitter*
Woodruff *is sweet*

Bouquets Garnis

HERB SAUCES

The two best known sauces must be mint and parsley sauce.

MINT SAUCE

250 ml/1 cup finely chopped mint
60 ml/¼ cup sugar
125 ml/½ cup water
250 ml/1 cup vinegar

1 Dissolve the sugar in the heated water and boil for a minute or two.

2 Add chopped mint and vinegar. Stir and leave for about 20 minutes before serving to allow the flavour to develop.

PARSLEY SAUCE

30 g/1 oz butter
2 tbsp plain flour
250 ml/1 cup milk
45 ml/3 tbsp finely chopped parsley
salt and pepper

1 Melt butter in small saucepan. Add flour, stir together and cook 1 minute over gentle heat.
2 Carefully stir in the milk and cook until sauce thickens. Add parsley and salt and pepper to taste.

PESTO SAUCE

This traditional Italian sauce is stirred into pasta or vegetable soup just before serving.

75 g/3 oz chopped basil leaves
3 garlic cloves
75 g/3 oz parmesan cheese, grated
80 ml/⅓ cup olive oil
pine-nuts or walnuts

1 Blend the basil, nuts and garlic into a puree. Add salt to taste. Stir in the grated cheese.
2 Add the olive oil very slowly, stirring with a wooden spoon. Stir until smooth and thick.

HERB BUTTER

Butter flavoured with herbs makes simple food delightfully different. It is used with baked potatoes, cooked vegetables, pasta and in sandwiches.

To each half-cup softened butter add 2 tsp of finely crushed dried herb or 2 tbsp minced fresh herbs. Mix well.

You can use it at once but the flavour develops better if it is left in the refrigerator overnight. It can also be stored in little pots or cartons in the freezer.

The famous maitre d'hotel butter is made by beating lemon juice and some finely chopped parsley and chervil, (more chervil than parsley), into butter.

BASIL AND GARLIC BUTTER

Blend some butter and Parmesan cheese in the food processor. When smooth, add some finely chopped basil leaves and finely minced garlic cloves. The proportions are a matter of taste so test as you go.

HERB CHEESE

This is made by heating grated cheese carefully in a saucepan incorporating as much of as many different herbs as one wishes—or only one sort. Chervil, chives, parsley, sage and tarragon make a nice mixture, Sage is fine on its own.

If you want something extra special, add some thickened cream and a dash or two of sherry before pouring the mixture into moulds.

When cold, remove from the moulds carefully and store wrapped in foil, in the refrigerator. Use Cheddar or a similar cheese.

Above: *Herbal butters and herbal rock salt will give a special flavour to any meal.*

Right: *When making cheese with herbs it is best to use Cheddar or similar cheeses.*

HERBAL SALT

To reduce the amount of salt in the diet try using a blend of salt and herbs. Don't use iodised salt for this.

1 Spread a thin layer of salt over a baking sheet, cover it with a layer of the fresh, chopped herbs of your choice and cover that with another thin layer of salt.

2 Put the sheet into a cool to moderate oven for 10 to 15 minutes, then check to see how the herb is crumbling. It has to be dried but not browned.

3 Put the mix through the blender to remove the lumps and to distribute the herbs through the salt. Store in well-sealed jars.

HERBAL VINEGAR

Herb vinegar is made by steeping well-bruised herbs in vinegar for about three weeks in a warm place. If, when tested, the flavour does not seem strong enough, strain the vinegar over a fresh lot of herbs and leave to steep for another two weeks or so. When the flavour is definite and pleasant, strain the vinegar carefully and bottle, preferably using a cork seal. You can use it more or less at once but it gets mellower with time.

Wine vinegar is the best one to use— the malt, white and cider vinegars have too much flavour of their own.

The vinegar can be used in salad dressing, mayonnaise and marinades, and a touch of it goes very well with green vegetables or sliced, cold beetroot. Balm, bergamot, chervil, chives, garlic, horseradish, marjoram, mint, salad burnet, thyme and tarragon are all suitable herbs to use.

They can be used in combination too but this has to be done with care for a strong tasting herb will overpower a weaker flavoured one.

Try:

Basil, borage and salad burnet.
Basil, chives, lovage and thyme.
Balm and tarragon.

RASPBERRY VINEGAR

Raspberry leaves are used medicinally and but the fruit can be used to make a vinegar which is not only medicinal but good for enlivening stewed fruit, particularly pears.

1 Steep fruit in wine vinegar for about ten days, giving it a stir every now and then with a wooden, not metal, spoon. Strain.
2 Using 400 g/14 oz sugar to 600 ml/1 pint liquid, heat gently until sugar has dissolved, then boil up quickly and keep at the boil for 10 minutes.
3 Skim the scum from the surface with great care. When the liquid is clear pour into hot, sterilised jars.
4 Seal when the vinegar is cool.

NASTURTIUM VINEGAR

This is particularly good with fish.

1 Fill a large jar with nasturtium flowers, add some salt and pepper, cayenne if you like, and enough vinegar to cover them. Cover the jar and leave for a few days.
2 The flowers will sink, leaving room for more vinegar. Top up, seal, and leave in a cool place for two weeks then strain and bottle the vinegar. Keep in

Top: *wine vinegar with thyme.*
Left: *Raspberry vinegar.*
Above: *Nasturtium vinegar.*

HERB OILS FOR COOKING

Green herbs can be kept steeped in oil for use in salads. Since oil is not a preservative they should not be kept too long. The more aromatic ones like basil, thyme and rosemary are best.

These oils can be used to coat meat, fish and poultry before grilling, roasting or barbecuing, and can be added to marinades and dressings.

A light coating on the frying pan in which you are making savoury pancakes will give them a livelier flavour.
You can also use the oil instead of butter or margarine when making savoury scones.

600 ml/1 pint or 2 1/4 cups sunflower oil
125 g/5 oz or 1 cup chopped herb

1 Bruise the leaves well and put in a glass jar and cover with sunflower oil.
2 Seal the jar and leave it in a warm place for at least two weeks, giving the contents a good shake every day. When ready, strain, pressing the herbs against the side of the jar with a wooden spoon to extract as much oil as possible. Bottle and seal.

Elegant bottles with herbs steeped in oil make an attractive and useful gift.

HERBS FOR OILS

Savoury: Basil, garlic, fennel, marjoram, mint, rosemary, tarragon, thyme and savory.

Sweet: Clove, pinks, lavender, lemon verbena and rose petals. Use in cakes or puddings.

HERB MUSTARDS

The seed of the black mustard has a hotter, stronger taste than that of the white variety.

A quick and simple way of making a mustard that should be used fairly quickly is to beat a little sugar and some wine or brandy into a little tin of plain bought mustard and then to add some cream and the very finely chopped herb of your choice.

If you are prepared to take a little more trouble you can grind together equal quantities of black and white mustard seeds (mortar and pestle or kitchen blender), add salt and pepper and some dried and pulverised orange or lemon peel (or a bit of both).

When smooth, add a touch of honey and some cider vinegar to taste and a sprinkle of tumeric for colour.

If you find the flavour too hot, cool it down with the addition of a little milk or mayonnaise.

Store in jars with good fitting lids or corks.

NUTTY MUSTARD

1 cup (250 ml) mustard seeds
1 tsp black peppercorns
salad oil, white wine and white wine vinegar
2 tsp dried, powdered herbs

1 Grind peppercorns, add some salt and stir in white wine to make a paste.
2 Grind mustard seeds with oil and vinegar to make a paste.
3 Combine the two. Stir. Add the herbs and stir yet again—very well.
4 Store in sterilised jars. Leave for at least a week before use.

FRENCH MUSTARD

1 Plain, dry, powdered mustard can be turned into French mustard by mixing it with a little sugar, some dry white wine or wine vinegar and a touch of salt. Leave the mixture to soak together for 2-3 hours.
2 Beat in 2-3 egg yolks and cook in the top of a double boiler over simmering hot water—in the way one makes lemon curd—stirring until it thickens, When cool keep covered in the refrigerator.

MULTI-MUSTARD

8 tbsp dry mustard powder
8 tbsp plain flour
4 tsp salt
9 tsp sugar
some cider vinegar containing pinch or two garlic powder, minced herbs—horseradish (for roast beef) tarragon (for fish) rosemary and thyme (for ham) sage (for cheese)

1 Mix dry ingredients together and bring to a smooth thick consistency with the gradual addition of the garlicky vinegar.
2 Divide into four parts. Add 1 tbsp finely grated horseradish to the first one, 1 tbsp finely chopped tarragon to the next, 1 tbsp finely chopped sage to the next and 1 tbsp chopped rosemary and thyme to the last.
3 Pot up separately in four little jars, label, and store for a month before using.

SALAD DRESSING

6 tbsp olive oil (or other oil if you prefer)
3 tbsp wine or cider vinegar
2 cloves peeled, minced garlic
1 tbsp finely crushed dried herbs or 3 of minced fresh herbs
salt and a touch of powdered mustard

Put all ingredients into a bottle and shake well. Leave for a while in the refrigerator before using.

TABOULEH

One of the best dishes which uses a quantity of herbs is Tabouleh. This is a real inducement to grow great beds of parsley.

250 ml/1 cup cracked wheat (bulgar)
500 ml/2 cups cold water
750 ml/3 cups finely chopped parsley, stems and leaves
63 ml/1/4 cup olive oil
3 tbsp lemon juice
125 ml/1/2 a cup finely chopped chives or spring onions
125 ml/1/2 a cup (or to taste) finely chopped mint
salt and pepper
2 skinned, chopped tomatoes

1 Soak the wheat in water for an hour. Drain and press to get as much water out as possible. Stir and lift the grains to get them nicely separated. Add all the green herbs, stirring well.
2 Mix oil and lemon juice and stir through the mixture. Just before serving add the tomatoes.

HERBAL MARINADE

This is very good for barbecued meat.

60 ml/1/4 cup olive oil
2 peeled garlic cloves
1 tbsp fresh, chopped basil
1 tbsp chopped rosemary and 1 of chives
10 balm leaves (lemon verbena will do instead)

Mix all ingredients in the blender, then pour over the meat and leave for several hours before cooking. Pour any remaining marinade over the meat as it cooks.

HERB BREAD

If bread-making with yeast seems daunting, make it with self-raising flour instead. It won't keep as well but since it is unlikely there will be any left at the end of the day that doesn't t matter.

THYME AND PUMPKIN DAMPER

750 ml/3 cups white self-raising flour
250 ml/1 cup oat or barley bran
3 tsp dried thyme
1 tbsp fresh well-chopped parsley
1 tsp each salt and sugar
2½ cups grated pumpkin (butternut)
250 ml/1 cup mixed milk and water
125 ml/½ cup olive oil

1 Mix sift flour, then add dry ingredients. Mix to a soft dough with the milk and oil. Knead on a floured surface until smooth. Handle lightly.
2 Bake in a well-greased 20 cm/8 inch casserole dish with a lid for an hour in a 200° C/400° F oven.

BASIL MUFFINS

750 ml/3 cups self raising flour
125 ml/½ cup chopped basil leaves
60 ml/¼ cup chopped sun-dried tomatoes
2 tbsp sugar
1 egg, beaten
60 ml/¼ cup olive oil
125 ml/1 ½ cup milk
black pepper

1 Beat oil, egg and milk together and pour gradually over mixed dry ingredients, stirring as you go. The mixture must not be too wet—keep it on the dry side.
2 Cook in well-greased muffin tin 15 minutes at 200° C/ 400° F

GARLIC BREAD STICKS

260 g/9 oz wholemeal self raising flour
black pepper
2 tsp mixed herbs
1 egg
200 ml/1 small cup milk
2 tbsp melted butter or oil
½ tsp crushed garlic
sesame seeds

1 Mix flour, herbs and plenty of ground black pepper.
2 Beat egg into milk and add to dry ingredients to make a soft dough.
3 On a floured board roll out the dough into a flat rectangle and cut into even-sized strips.
4 Lightly roll strips between the palms to make into conventional "stick" shape. Cut to size.
5 Put melted butter or oil into a tray, add garlic and mix.
6 Roll the strips in the mixture and arrange in pan. Sprinkle with sesame seeds and cook in a hot oven (220° C/425° F) for 10-15 minutes.

ROSEMARY AND OLIVE BREAD

780 g/1lb 10 oz white plain flour
2 tbsp powdered milk
1 tsp salt
2 tsp sugar
30 g/1 oz dried yeast
warm water
rosemary leaves
olives, halved, black or green

1 Mix dry ingredients. Crumble yeast into 125 ml/half a cup warm water and mix well.
2 Add oil and yeast mixture to dry ingredients, adding more warm water if needed to make a soft dough.
3 Turn on to a floured surface and knead well until dough becomes springy. Cover and keep in a warm place for 15 minutes.
4 Divide into two and roll into flat rectangles. Put dough on a greased oven tray and leave, lightly covered with a cloth, in a warm place for nearly an hour or until it has risen to double the thickness.
5 When risen, poke holes in the dough right down to the tray and put a tiny sprig of rosemary or a sliced olive in each one. Bake at 220° C /425° F 20-25 minutes.

HERBS AND FRUIT

- ***Angelica leaves*** *in a fruit salad*
- ***A bay leaf*** *in a baked custard*
- ***Bergamot leaves*** *in almost any stewed fruit*
- ***Lavender flowers*** *with custards and ice-cream and stewed berry jam*
- ***Balm leaves*** *in cakes and pies to give a lemon flavour and chopped over a fruit salad or an iced drink*
- ***Mint leaves*** *in a fruit salad*
- ***Sage leaves****, or* ***thyme leaves*** *very sparingly with stewed pears or apple*
- ***Woodruff*** *leaves with berry fruits*

Right: *Herb bread*

GROSS
TARE
HARIO
MCA-5

Herbal Tea, Wine & Beer

Herbal Tea

Herbal teas are flavourful, refreshing and can positively contribute to health. They do not contain tannin, caffeine or fluoride, but have properties that can soothe, refresh, and invigorate; they make a valuable contribution to the diet if taken on a regular basis.

What did our ancestors in the Western world use as a non-alcoholic drink before travellers brought home from China leaves of the bush that became known as *camellia sinensis* and the long love-affair with "tea" began?

Tea was not known until the mid-sixteen hundreds when Catherine de Braganza, Charles the Second's sad little wife, introduced it to the English Court as an alternative to the intoxicating beverages which were so freely available. The royal patronage ensured that "taking tea" became quite the thing, and before long the fashion had ensnared many members of the upper and middle classes. But it was too expensive for poorer people and the tea they drank for comfort and relaxation was made from the leaves and flowers they gathered from the meadows and hedgerows.

There was woodruff—a tiny plant with sweet-scented star-shaped flowers and dark green leaves with strangely hooked edges—meadowsweet, with a froth of fragrant blossom and leaves that dried, carried the scent of new-mown hay—melilot, beloved of the bees, the sweet briar rose. In the "physick" garden they grew herbs for medicines—sage, rosemary, thyme and many more. There was a wide choice of plants from which to make infusions which contained neither tannin nor caffeine but which could brighten a tired and solitary drinker or enliven a social occasion.

Today we think of Indian tea as being "real" tea and anything else as being a departure from the norm. The appellation "herbal tea" sounds vaguely accusing, as though it must be made clear that it isn't all one might think. And "herbal" somehow makes one think of a prescription. How much nicer, now that interest in alternative ingredients

Left, Opposite: *Herbal teas are flavourful, refreshing and contribute to health. They do not contain tannin, caffeine or fluoride, but have properties that can soothe, refresh and invigorate.*

"LIBERTY TEA"

Combine equal parts raspberry leaves, elderberries and elderflowers.

Blend the herbs and store in an air tight tin or jar away from the heat or sunlight.

Take by heaping 1 teaspoon of herb mixture for each cup of boiling water and infusing for 5-10 minutes. Sweeten with honey or maple syrup for an authentic taste.

for the "cup that cheers" has become so wide, to use the old name "tisane" which is distinctive and hints at something which is beguilingly different.

In the seventeen hundreds, China tea was popular both in England and her American colony to whom she exported it in large amounts. The import tax was heavy and grew heavier and the colonists finally decided they had had enough and refused to let the ships unload their cargo. Tempers flared and over three hundred chests of tea were slung into the harbour in an event which became known as the Boston Tea Party and which played a considerable part in provoking the War of Independence.

Deprived of their tea there was nothing the colonists could do but fall back on the plants they knew and to experiment with others. It became a matter of national pride to show how well they could do without the wretched stuff. Recipes for what they called Liberty tea sound very appetising. One called for two parts of raspberry leaves to one part each of bee balm flowers and elderflowers and elderberries. Another for equal parts of wood betony, goldenrod, red clover flowers and leaves of the redroot bush

It is surely not difficult to be creative. One can buy from a herbalist dried plants native to other parts of the world and mix them with our own dried garden ones.

A HERBAL TEA GARDEN

A small tea garden close to the house makes it easy to make a quick cup of tea.

The herbs that give pleasant drinks are mostly friendly ones and will happily grow together in the same bed. But not mint or parsley. They are better grown in their own beds. Mint needs more water than most other herbs and can take over if growth is not controlled and parsley always seems to grow more willingly when it has no herbal neighbours.

Angelica, basil, bergamot, borage, catmint, chamomile, golden rod, horehound, jasmine, lemon verbena, lovage, marjoram, mint, parsley, rosemary, sage, sweet cicely, thyme and woodruff are all easily grown herbs which make a pleasant tea.

Some have a more robust flavour and are less sweet than others; lovage, parsley, rosemary, sage and thyme, for instance. These herbs make a tea which is good with a salty biscuit and a sliver of cheese rather than sweet cake or biscuits.

The soil for a herb garden should not be rich, particularly if the herbs grown are the aromatic ones native to the rocky, sun-scorched areas around the Mediterranean Sea. These herbs are used to struggling for life, and hardship seems to bring out the best in them for given a rich soil and plenty of moisture they become limper and less flavoursome. So we don't pamper herbs but we don't treat them all alike either for they do have their preferences.

TEA HERBS

For full sun
basil, bergamot, catmint, lemongrass, parsley, rosemary, sage, thyme

For dappled shade
angelica, balm, borage, lovage, parsley

For dry conditions
rosemary, thyme

For moist conditions
angelica, bergamot, lovage, mint
The soil should drain well— they hate having their feet in a puddle.

MAKING HERBAL TEA

Once free of the notion that the only tea to drink is the conventional Indian or Chinese brew, a whole world of flavours and possibilities opens up. One can buy herbal teas, single or blended, and explore a range of tastes.

Using fresh herbs

It is a real joy to nip into the garden, cut off a few leaves from a green and healthy plant, and, no more than ten minutes later, be enjoying a fragrant cup of tea.

"Fresh" is a lovely word. The dictionary says it means "retaining the original properties unimpaired". The fresh herbs give us the very best of themselves in that clear, clean liquid.

Tastes vary. Some people like weak tea, some like it strong so it is as well to experiment a bit. Herbs taken straight from the garden can have a stronger taste than ones bought at the market and kept in the fridge for a few days. One to two teaspoonsful of fresh, well-chopped herb to one cup of near boiling water is a useful yardstick. I tend to be overgenerous with the herb on the grounds that if you find the tea too strong you can always dilute it and feed the surplus to thirsty pot plants, but you can't do much with a wishy-washy brew.

The teapot I use when making a pot just for myself holds 600 mls/l pint of water, enough for three cups of tea.

I use three good heaped teaspoonsful of fresh herbs to a full pot and let it stand for five minutes. When I pour out the first cup, I top up the pot.

This is left to stand while I relax and enjoy doing nothing at all but sitting quietly, sipping and thinking.

The tea is still hot enough when I need a second cup.

The remainder is left in the pot to go cold. It provides a pleasant drink later on. Any left is fed to the plants or compost heap.

Some people enjoy the taste of the tea "neat". Others like the addition of honey and lemon. Again it is a matter of experimentation. Herbs such as lemon thyme and lemon verbena have their own clean and pleasant taste and need no additives, but others can be improved by them.

A GLOSSARY OF TEA TERMS

Decoction: *A beverage made by simmering herbs for 10-20 minutes. This method is generally used to bring out the full flavour of roots and seeds and for some flowers and leaves such as lemon verbena.*

Flavoured tea: *Tea which has been flavoured, usually with essential oils of fruits, spices or herbs.*

Green tea: *China tea that has been dried but not oxidised or fermented.*

Infusion: *A beverage made by pouring boiling water over herb leaves or flowers and steeping them for 5-10 minutes to release the aromatic oils. A general recipe is 1 teaspoon of dried herb or 3 teaspoons of fresh, crushed herbs per cup of boiling water. For a stronger drink add more herb but don't steep the tea longer as this may cause the tea to become bitter.*

You use an infuser to steep the herb. This is a small perforated metal ball used to hold the tea leaves while they steep in the hot water.

Sun tea: *Tea made by adding tea leaves to cold water in a lidded glass jar and leaving in full sunshine for 4 to 8 hours. The sun warms the water and causes the gentle release of the aromatic oils. Teas made by this method have a very smooth flavour and rarely turn cloudy in the refrigerator as steeped teas sometimes do.*

Tisane: *An infusion, originally of barley but now usually of fresh or dried herbs, used as a beverage or medicinal tea.*

Ensure that your teas are kept in airtight containers to preserve the flavour.

Infusers are used to steep the herb. They hold leaves or herb mixtures while the hot water moves through the holes. Don't infuse too long or the tea will be bitter.

Using Dried Herbs

Home-dried herbs are usually quite strong and little more than half a teaspoonful, per cup or 2 5 g/l oz to a 600 m/l pint pot will do. But there are no hard and fast rules as strength can vary from one drying to another. I find too that if you are using a blend of herbs the strength of one of them will predominate from brew to brew. The results, though variable, are always pleasing.

The important thing when making herb tea is to put the teapot lid on firmly so that the essential oils are not carried away in the steam.

It is best to use a pot even when making just one cup of tea. You can buy some very pretty little ones.

Some people use infusers when making just one cup but an infuser doesn't always hold the amount of fresh herb necessary and its shape doesn't allow the cup to be covered to keep in the steam.

Drying concentrates the flavour of a herb considerably so you will always need less by weight, though not by bulk, of the fresh herb.

I don't find the old maxim for ordinary tea—"one for each nob and one for the pot" works very well for me so I am hesitant about giving precise amounts. Much depends on individual taste and also the way the herb was gathered and stored. The bought one-cup sachets are usually too strong and I can make three cups out of one. Other people could find the taste woeful.

If, when you begin to experiment with herbal teas, you don't find them as flavoursome as you would like, try them mixed with a little China, Jasmine or Earl Grey tea—not a lot, just enough to make the presence felt. Raspberry and strawberry teas give added flavour too but they contain tannin.

Chamomile, mint, lemon balm, lemon verbena, lemongrass, lime, sage, rosemary, thyme, rose hip, bergamot, catmint, hyssop are all aromatic plants which make pleasant teas, but not all sweet-smelling ones do. The geranium leaves which carry the scent of apple or nutmeg are not nice at all—the rose geranium holds its scent though, perhaps a little too well for a cup of tea on its own. A leaf or two in blends of other teas can be very pleasant.

HERBAL TEAS FOR HEALTH

The comfort given by a steaming hot cup of "real" tea and the temporary lift given by the caffeine it contains is dear to the heart of many people. When pleasure is so great and habit so engrained who bothers about the stain tea leaves on the pot? Tannin is used for tanning leather—tea contains tannin—what does it do to the stomach walls? Devoted tea-drinkers will ignore such questions but can they not be tempted to try the brew of other herbs too? They taste pleasant and are tannin free.

Angelica tea: Drink it if you feel a cold coming on or are feeling rheumaticky.
Balm tea: Unsweetened, this lemony drink will ease a cold or head-ache.
Basil tea: If you get the shivers for no apparent reason, make a tea from the leaves and flowering tips and sit quietly and listen to soft music as you drink it.
Bergamot tea: If you have a sore throat make a strong brew and use as a gargle.
Borage tea: If you feel "off" this cucumber—tasting tea will liven you.
Catmint tea: Drink it when you have wind, hiccups or menstruation is late.
Chamomile tea: This is one of the great soothers. It eases upset stomachs, strained nerves and prevents nightmares. Parents with children cutting teeth or suffering from ear-ache should make a big pot for the whole family.
Golden rod tea: Tastes of aniseed and helps with high blood pressure.
Lovage tea: Good for the burps.
Mint tea: Good for a bad digestion.
Parsley tea: Good for cystitis and menstrual cramps.
Rosemary tea: Drink it when nerves are strained and a headache won't go away.
Sage tea: Sage contains oestrogen.
Thyme tea: Is good for the chest and makes a bracing tonic.

CHAMOMILE TEA

600 ml/1 pint boiling water
1 tbsp dried chamomile flower heads
Caster sugar or honey

1 Put the chamomile flowers into a teapot. Pour on the boiling water and leave to infuse for about 5 minutes, or longer if you want a stronger flavour.

2 Strain the tea and add a small amount of caster sugar or honey and stir to dissolve.

DANDELION TEA

1 tsp dried dandelion leaves
dried orange peel
boiling water
honey

1 Place dried dandelion leaves in an infuser. Place in a cup of boiling water and infuse.

2 Add dried orange peel and honey to taste.

A simple tonic tea with medicinal value for skin and liver problems. High in iron.

Herbal Wine & Beer

Old country recipes specify an amount of fresh ingredients for beer and wine that today we will find difficult to assemble. And if you have to buy parsley, the price charged for a small bunch could make you think hard before undertaking the enterprise. However, dried herbs work well and the amount needed is considerably less than half the fresh one.

You will need

- a large enamelled pan for boiling the brew
- a large plastic bucket or bowl
- a large piece of gauze or similar material for straining
- a funnel
- bottles
- a fermentation lock available from home-brewing stores is useful.

GINGER BEER

The old-fashioned way of making ginger beer for the family was to use a "plant".

Making the plant:

1 tsp each sugar and ground ginger
250 ml/1 large cup cold water
more sugar and ground ginger

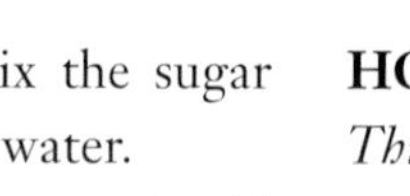

1 To make the "plant" mix the sugar and ginger with the cup of water.
2 Each morning for the next week add another teaspoon each of sugar and ginger. At the end of the week strain off the liquid and keep the sediment safely in a jar. This is the plant and it will stay alive for use again if you feed it each day with some sugar and ginger.

Making the beer

1 Heat together 750 ml/3 cups water, 780 g/3-4 cups sugar and juice of 3 lemons until the sugar is dissolved.
2 Add the "plant" liquid and enough cold water to bring the quantity up to 4.5 litres/8 pints. Stir well. Bottle, but not up to the top of the bottle or you could have an explosion. Drink in 3 weeks.

HOREHOUND BEER

This is medieval as well as tasty.

60 g/1 oz well-chopped leaves and stems
30 g/$^{1}/_{2}$ oz well-bruised fresh ginger root
Juice 1 lemon
450 g/1 lb brown sugar
2 tbsp fresh yeast
1 tsp treacle
2 pinches cream of tartar

1 Cover the leaves and ginger with water and bring slowly to the boil in a large heavy pan over controlled heat. Maintain at a steady rolling boil for about 30 minutes, occasionally pressing the contents against the side of the pan to help to extract the goodness.
2 Take from the heat, add the sugar and enough boiling water to bring the liquid content up to 4 litres/7 pints. Stir well until sugar is dissolved. Leave to stand for 10 minutes, then add lemon juice, treacle and cream of tartar.
3 When liquid is cool add the well crumbled yeast. Strain twice—then bottle, leaving the bottles in a dark place for 3 days before corking them.

There is something delightfully earthy about making your own delicious ginger or horehound beer.

NETTLE BEER

Bucket young nettle tops
90 g/3 oz sugar
36 l/63 pints water
2 heaped tbsp ground ginger
2 flat tbsp cream of tartar
30 g/1 oz fresh yeast or 15 g/½ oz dried yeast

You need a very large saucepan for this, or you could boil up nettles in two lots. You also need a large container in which the beer can stand.

1 Boil up nettles and ginger and keep at a rolling boil for 20 minutes. Strain on to the sugar and stir until it dissolves.
2 Leave until fairly cool then add the cream of tartar and stir. Leave until barely warm, add yeast and do not stir. Cover and leave overnight.
3 Skim the surface, strain twice, bottle and seal well. Leave for a day or two but not too long. When you pour out he beer, do it carefully as there will be sediment at the bottom of the bottle. Old fashioned jug or basin sets come in very useful.

DANDELION WINE

A large non-metal container is needed and a small barrel, a siphon and bottles. These can all be obtained from wine-makers' shops.

enough flowerheads to fill a 2.5 l/ 4½ pint container (don't include any green part of the plant and remove stem and calyx)
2.5 l/4 pints water
725 g/1½ lb sugar
2 lemons, thinly peeled rind (oranges if you prefer)
15 g/½ oz well-bruised ginger root
15 g/½ oz fresh yeast

1 Soak the flowers covered in water for a day and a night. Lift the cover and give the contents a stir every now and then, re-covering the container quickly.
2 Pour into a large saucepan, add peel and ginger and boil, retaining the rolling boil for half an hour. Put the sugar in a large container and strain the liquid over it using a large sieve or very safely anchored sheet of gauze.
3 The heat of the liquid should dissolve the sugar. If you need to help it gently use a wooden spoon. Taste when cool and add some fruit juice if you think the flavour is not strong enough.
4 Cream the yeast and add to the liquid. Do another gentle stir and cover the container with a cloth. The liquid will froth and rise and continue doing so for about two days.

When it has stopped hiccuping and making gas bubbles, pour it into a small barrel and bung lightly, tightening the bung after a few days. Forget it for 2 months then carefully siphon the liquid into bottles. Cork tightly or screw down well and leave for 6 months.

COLTSFOOT WINE

Coltsfoot wine also requires a barrel and a bung—and patience. You have to leave it in the barrel for 6 months but it's good when you open it.

1 kg/2 lb coltsfoot flowers
1.5 kg/3 lb white sugar
juice and thinly peeled rind of 2 lemons
4.5 l/8 pints water
handful stoned raisins
15 g/½ oz fresh yeast
slice of toast

1 Bring water containing sugar and fruit rind to the boil and hold till rinds have softened and given up their flavour.
2 Mix flowers, raisins and fruit juice in a large container and pour the boiling liquid over them when it is at the height of the boil. Stir with a long wooden spoon and leave until just warm.
3 Spread the yeast on toast and float it on the liquid and leave, under a light, covered for 5 days in a warm place.
4 Using a very fine sieve or fine muslin, strain into the barrel, keeping back the last of the liquid. Insert the bung lightly. Put the reserved liquid in a jug and keep it covered in a warm place.
Listen to the barrel every day. When you can no longer hear the ferment agitation, add the reserved liquid and hammer the bung in. The wine will not be ready for 6 months.

COWSLIP WINE

1 kg/2 lb fresh flower-heads
1 5 kg/3 lb white sugar
4.5 litres/8 pints boiling water
Rind and juice 2 lemons (or oranges)
60 g/2 oz fresh yeast

1 Boil the sugar and water until slightly syrupy, then pour it over the fruit rinds and juice. Leave till just warm then add the flowers and yeast and stir well. Cover the container with a cloth and visit it, morning and evening, for 3 days to give it a good stir.
2 Carefully strain the liquid into the barrel, keeping some on one side and bung the barrel loosely. Listen to the barrel every day and when all has become quiet, add the reserved liquid which you have been keeping warm and covered, hammer down the bung and leave for 10 to 12 weeks.

ELDERFLOWER WINE

1 kg/2 lb elderflowers
1 kg/2 lb sugar
4 litre/7 pints water
28 g/1oz fresh yeast
juice of 2 lemons (or oranges)
slice of toast

1 Avoid bruising the flowers when collecting them. Boil them in the water for 20 minutes. Strain and discard the flowers, making certain there are no bits left.
2 Add sugar and fruit juice to the liquid and heat gently until sugar is dissolved, then boil for another 20 minutes. Strain into a large container and allow to cool before floating the toast carrying the crumbled yeast on it. Cover and leave in a warm place for a day before bottling.

ELDERFLOWER CHAMPAGNE

2 good handfuls elderflowers—unbruised
1 lemon
2 tbsp white vinegar
700 g/1½ lb sugar
4 litres/7 pints water

1 Grate the lemon rind, squeeze the juice and add to the elderflowers, sugar and vinegar. Stir. Add the water and stir again. Cover the container and leave to stand for a day. Strain twice and bottle securely—corks or screwtops.
2 Leave in a dark place for 3 weeks before opening.

PARSLEY WINE

450 g/1lb parsley, stalks and all
4 litres/7 pints boiling water
28 g/10 oz scraped and chopped ginger root
1.5 kg/3 lb white sugar
juice and thinly-pared peel
2 lemons (or oranges)
15 g/½ oz fresh yeast
slice of toast

1 Put the parsley in a big container and pour boiling water over it. Cover and leave to stand for 24 hours.
2 Strain and discard the parsley. Add ginger root and fruit juice to the parsley water and bring to the boil and hold gently rolling, for 25 minutes.
3 Put sugar and fruit juice in a large container and pour the boiled liquid over it. The heat should dissolve the sugar— if it doesn't, help it along very, very gently with a wooden spoon. When nearly cool crumble the yeast onto the toast and float on the surface of the liquid.
4 Cover, and leave undisturbed in a moderately warm place, not too hot or draughty, for 5 days. By then the yeast should have finished fermenting. Strain and bottle carefully and seal lightly. After a few days if there are no signs of the yeast still "working", tighten the screwtops or hammer down the corks.

MARIGOLD WINE

marigold flowers—enough to fit into a large 2.5 litre/4 pint jug
2 oranges—juice and thinly-cut rind
1 lemon—juice and thinly cut rind
1.5 k/3 lb sugar
4.5 litres/8 pints water
15 g/½ oz fresh yeast or 7.5 g/¼ oz. dried yeast

1 Boil water and sugar and pour over the flowers and fruit rind and juice in a large ceramic jug or bowl. Leave to cool. Add yeast and stir well. Cover and leave in a warm place for a week.
2 Strain the liquid into a ceramic container and leave it, covered, until all sound of fermentation is over—this will be at least a month. Bottle. Wait for a week or longer before opening.

MEADOWSWEET FIZZ

1 Take equal quantities of meadowsweet, agrimony and wood betony leaves to weigh 75 g/2½ oz and boil them up in 4.5 litres/8 pints water
2 Strain boiling liquid over 500 g/ 1 lb sugar and make sure the sugar dissolves. Leave till cool and then bottle, leaving space at the top of the bottle and the cork or screwtop loose.

After a week the natural yeasts contained in the plants will have fermented and the fizz be ready to drink. Don't keep it too long.

GINGER WHISKY

This is warming although it is drunk cold, and is a drink to keep in small bottles, well-hidden.

1 Pour a litre of whisky into a wide-mouthed vacuum flask or similar container. Add about 28 g/1 oz well-bruised ginger root, 28 g/1 oz caraway seeds, 250 g/2 cups seedless raisins, 780 g/3 cups sugar and the juice and very finely peeled rind of 1 or 2 lemons. Shake well and seal.
2 Shake each day for 2 weeks. Strain and bottle.

Modern home-brewing containers are made from easily cleanable glass or plastic, the old ones which look so attractive and full of character must be scrupulously cleansed.

BREW~
DATE BOTTLED

Lavender
Water

Herbal Craft & Decorating

DYEING WITH HERBS

Plant dyeing is a very ancient skill—it was known in China three thousand years before the birth of Christ. The rich glowing colours of the robes worn by the ancient Egyptians came from the plants they grew especially for the purpose. Chemical dye did not make its appearance until the nineteenth century and since it was cheap and easy to use was soon taken up commercially and the natural dyes largely fell into disuse. Townspeople no longer dyed their own clothes—they took them to the dyers; but in rural communities the old traditions held— particularly in isolated ones.

The spinners and weavers of the offshore islands of Scotland and Ireland and Scandinavian communities have kept the old methods alive and there has always been a demand for their work.

There is a depth and glow about a natural dye—a mellowness The soft browns and greys, the muted yellows and greens, the hazy reds and tawny golds have a delicate subtlety.

Flowers from which we can obtain dyes grow all around us—weeds like dandelion, dock, horsetail and nettle—garden flowers like agrimony, chamomile, golden rod, marigold, tansy, meadowsweet, gorse elder—and many more. Even parsley and onions can be used. Red berries are especially good.

Herbs can be bought dried for dyeing—but if fresh ones are available always use those.

It takes a lot of herbs to provide a strong clear dye. If you plan to grow your own make preparation for large beds of massed plants.

The colours produced are not uniform. It depends on when the herbs were picked, whether they were young or mature, what the weather was like on the day, and on the soil and water.

There are no certainties.

The colour of natural dyes is more subdued than those of bought ones and you can never be sure you will get quite the same colour twice.

Cotton, linen and synthetic materials are chancey and best left to professionals. For the home dyer it is better to start with wool, preferably in hanks. Silk can come later.

You need herbs weighing at least as much as the wool to be dyed and twice the weight of silk.

Dripping skeins of hand-dyed, home-spun wool dry in the breeze.

You will need

- scales
- 2 large saucepans (stainless steel for preference but not aluminium or plain iron)
- three or four buckets (for soaking, rinsing etc) or access to large sinks
- rubber gloves
- strong glass or wooden rod for stirring
- a strong wooden rod on which to hang wool hanks to dry
- large colander or sieve
- a mordant

Method

1 Weigh article to be dyed.
2 Collect at least twice the weight, or more, of the fresh herb needed.
3 Chop herb, bruise stems and leave to soak in rainwater overnight. If you have to use tapwater, add a touch of vinegar. Make wool into smallish hanks. Tie the hanks with string securely but loosely in several places. The dye must have access to all sides of the yarn and the yarn must not tangle.
4 Scour the wool. This is done by soaking the hanks for an hour in water containing some liquid detergent—or soft soap and ammonia. The water should be about 50° C/130° F.
5 Drain away the water and squeeze wool gently to get as much water out as possible.
6 Soak in cooler water containing detergent or soft soap for a further hour. If the wool is very oily you may have to leave it to soak overnight and rinse it several times. this is done to take oil out of the wool.
7 When the wool has been scoured sufficiently well the dyeing process can continue or the wool can be dried and stored for a later session.

If wool is to be stored

Handle the wool gently as it is lifted from the final rinse. Press water out with the flat of the hand and then put wool into a pillowcase and spin in the dryer at half-speed. Hang the hanks on a rod in a warm, airy spot away from sun and heat so that complete drying is slow and natural.

If dyeing process is to be continued

Wool does not absorb water readily so although the scoured wool has been well rinsed to get rid of the oil and is damp, it has to be thoroughly soused before the next process.

HERB COLOURS FOR DYING

Herbs for red dye
lady's bedstraw roots, oregano, tea leaves

Herbs for pink dye
sorrel roots

Herbs for yellow dye
agrimony, chamomile, comfrey, golden rod, horsetail, juniper, marigold, onion skins, St John's wort, yarrow

Herbs for orange dye
lily-of-the-valley leaves, onion skins, tansy shoots

Herbs for blue dye
elecampne roots, cornflowers

Herbs for green dye
coltsfoot leaves, hyssop, larkspur, onion, sorrel, sweet cicely

Herbs for brown dye
juniper berries, tea leaves

Mordanting

1 25 g/1 oz mordant (alum) and a small amount of cream of tartar will make enough to dye 100 g/4 oz wool.

2 Dissolve the required amount of mordant in hot water and stir into a large saucepan of water deep enough to cover the wool to be dyed.

3 Heat until warm then gently tip in the soaking wet wool. Slowly bring the water to simmering point. It should take about an hour. Hold on the simmer for another hour.

The wool will not shrink or felt. BUT IT MUST NOT BE POKED AROUND OR STIRRED. Take saucepan off heat and leave to cool.

4 While this is going on,put the herbs and the water in which they have been soaking into a large saucepan and slowly bring the water to the boil. Reduce to a simmer until the water takes on a darker colour than the one you wish the dyed garment to be. This will take 2 or more hours. Take saucepan from the heat, strain water and leave to cool.

5 Lift wool from the mordant water with a glass rod and slide it into the dye water. Put the dye water back over heat and very slowly bring it back to the boil. It will take about an hour.

6 Let the water cool till wool can be handled. (wear gloves).

Lift the hanks from the water and gently squeeze away excess dye.

7 Rinse hanks in a bucket of hot water. Rinse again in a bucket of warm water. Give a final rinse in a bucket of cold water. The rinsing should not be done under running water.

8 Squeeze and blot hanks to rid them of some of the water then hang them on a wooden rod in a cool, airy place, away from the sun, to dry.

MORDANTS

A mordant is a water-soluble metal salt that will help to set the colour of the dye and prevent fading.

The choice is between:

- ***Alum** (aluminium potassium sulphate)*

Cream of tartar is often used in conjunction with alum or iron. Alum is the least toxic and gives a strong bright colour.

- ***Tin** (stannous chloride)*
- ***Chrome** (potassium dichromate)*
- ***Iron** (ferrous sulphate)*

If the colour is too strong after using alum, it can be softened and deepened by adding some iron (ferrous sulphate to the dye bath.

The amounts used are great—2g alum is enough for 20 litres/35 pints dye water.

Below: *Wear your apron, there is a lot of splashing.*

lbs
Krups Ideal
iron

PRINTING WITH HERBS

Leonardo da Vinci wrote of nature prints in the sixteenth century.

Botanists needing to have a record of the plants they studied, held their specimens over a candle or oil lamp until the smoke had blackened them and then pressed them against a sheet of paper. The impression, though crude, was accurate. As time went on, printer's ink was found to give sharper and more detailed impressions and quite a comprehensive record of individual plant life was made. As printing techniques advanced, half-tone printing and colour photography took over—there was no more need for that laborious inking, but it is a technique which can be happily used today for printing for one's personal pleasure.

Prints made this way have a simple old-world charm. They can be used to decorate cards, writing paper, covered boxes, journals. Once you become proficient you will find you are producing prints you are happy to frame and hang on the wall.

Above, Opposite: *Projects printed with herbs.*

Preparation

On a clear, dry day make a collection of leaves and sprigs and put them between paper and the pages of a thick book, one specimen to a page. Weigh the book down. The object is to make them as flat as possible. Single leaves will soon be flat—sprigs could take two days.

The best paper to use is newsprint which is soft and absorbent. Soft copying paper works well too.

You can use either water-soluble ink or watercolour paint.

The methods are slightly different. A sheet of glass is needed for both of them.

THE INK METHOD

1 Cover the sheet of glass with ink.
2 Place specimen on the glass, underside up.
3 Using a soft brush, and being careful to keep the specimen in position, brush it all over with ink, starting from the centre. If it is a leaf, follow the line of the veins—if it is a sprig make certain all the stem is covered. Always work from inward to outward.
4 Lift the specimen with tweezers and place it on the newsprint, underside down. Be very precise.
5 Cover the specimen with some kitchen paper and anchor it in place by pressing the centre down with the pad of a finger.
6 With the pad of the fore-finger press the specimen down, working from the inside out, following all the contours. Do not rub. The action is downward press, lift, downward press, lift. Stems need the most careful treatment. **7** Remove covering paper and, using tweezers, lift off the specimen.

If you have used too much ink the print will be dark and without detail.

If you have used too little or have not pressed all parts of the specimen evenly the print will be pale and spotty.

If you have allowed the specimen to move the print will be blurred.

Try another one straight away.

USING WATERCOLOUR PAINT

The newsprint has to be damp. Place it between damp paper towels and cover with plastic while you are preparing the specimens.

1 Cover the sheet of glass with water colour paint the consistency of double cream. Make the layer as even as you can.
2 Place the specimen on the glass, underside up, and, keeping it in position, brush over with a thin coating of soapy water. This will help the paint to stick.
3 Paint the specimen all over, brushing from the inside out. Keep the paint even and cover specimen thoroughly.
4 Remove the newsprint from between the damp paper which should be evenly moist. Then follow the process as for the ink method.

To begin with it is best to use only one colour, but as dexterity increases several can be used.

Specimens can be used several times. Let the ink or paint dry and put them away until needed again. But you can't do it with fragile flowers.

HERBAL PAPER

A textured paper with herbs embedded in the fibres makes a good mount for drawings, paintings and photographs. Scented herbs in the fibres makes it an attractive drawer liner.

Recycling computer print-outs and old newspapers tidies the place up and gives rubbish a new life.

Method

1 Tear up the paper into small pieces and leave to soak overnight in warm water.

2 Make 2 wooden frames, writing paper size or larger to suit your need, and cover one of them tightly with strong nylon net. Tacks or staples will hold it in place.

3 The following day liquidize the pulp in the blender, a little at a time. Use 1 litre/1½ pints of water to 3 tablespoons pulp plus a touch of starch to "size" the paper.

4 Pour it all into a deep, wide bucket or plastic bath.

5 Place the frame without net over the frame with net and, keeping them firmly together, dip them, vertically into the bucket.

6 Keeping the frames beneath the pulp, tilt them to the horizontal and lift upwards, slowly and steadily and bring them out of the pulp still at the horizontal.

7 Place on thick, spread newspaper to drain.

8 Take away the top frame and scatter your chosen herbs over the pulp. A thick scatter of scented potpourri will keep to make lovely drawer liners.

Delicate flower petals, bits of dried fern, bits of torn onion skin, a single blossom, will make delightful paper for any purpose you please.

9 When the paper is dry, slide a palette knife underneath it and lift it carefully from the frame. The frame now has to be cleaned before it is used again.

Paper textured and scented with herbs makes beautiful stationery.

LAVENDER WANDS

A really old-fashioned way of scenting drawers and wardrobes is the lavender wand—a bunch of lavender spikes wrapped in tightly woven ribbon. They are easy to make and a collection of them in a pretty box will provide a delightful present.

Materials:

20 young, fresh, long-stalked spikes of lavender flowers

Don't use old ones, they are not pliable enough.

1 m/39 in narrow lavender-coloured ribbon.

1 Arrange lavender stalks in equal lengths.

2 Tie the ribbon tightly just below the flower spikes with one end of the ribbon short and the other long. The short end should be about 20 cm/8 inches.

3 Take the long end of the ribbon upwards to extend beyond the top of the flower spikes.

4 Bend 10 spikes, in groups of two upwards, from just below the knotted ribbon and arrange them to enclose the flower heads completely. Trim off any surplus.

5 Starting at the top and working down, weave the long end of the ribbon through them horizontally. Pull it tight—the flowers will shrink as they dry. Cover them completely.

6 Tie the two ends of ribbon into a bow.

TUSSIE-MUSSIES

The habit of carrying a tiny, perfumed nosegay was, in times gone by, a lady's way both of looking elegant and warding off the unpleasant smell of open drains and attack by germs. In addition the choice of flowers and leaves spelt out a message.

Materials:
- a central flower (traditionally a large red rosebud)
- small flowers—lavender pansy, marjoram, angelica, catmint violets, sweet peas, sage, tansy
- leaves—feathery ones such as fennel and southernwood, grey ones such as santolina. Rosemary, mint, balm, verbena, sweet-scented geraniums etc
- thin green string
- patterned paper doily and some ribbon

1 Holding the rosebud (or whatever flower you choose) firmly, place some of the smaller leaves around it in a tight circle and tie the stalks together with the green string to hold everything in place.

2 Encircle the little posy with small flowers and tie in place.

3 Finish off with a circle of the larger leaves and secure.

4 Make a hole in the centre of the doily and poke the flower stems through. Settle the nosegay in place at the back of the doily and tie in place with long pieces of pretty ribbon. Curl the ends into streamers.

Reading a tussie-mussie

Rose	*I love you*
Rosemary	*Your presence revives me*
Pansy	*You are always in my mind*
Angelica	*Your love lights up my life*
Verbena	*You enchant me*
Thyme	*All I want is to be with you*
Sage	*I will suffer any-thing for you*
Marjoram	*Your passion makes me blush*
Agrimony	*I am grateful*
Forget-me-not	*You are my true love*
Lily-of-the-valley	*Happiness has returned*
Ivy	*I am true*
Thyme	*Take courage*
Elder	*I send compassion*
Lemon Balm	*I offer you sympathy*
Sweet Basil	*Good wishes*
Rosemary	*Remembrance*
Pansy	*My thoughts are with you*

A FRESH HERBAL WREATH

Festive wreaths celebrating birthdays, wedding anniversaries, weddings, christenings and all joyful occasions are easily made, and if herbs and flowers which dry easily are used, will give pleasure for quite a long time.

Method

Gather all the herbs you plan to use to cover the wreath.

You can use sprigs of bay, lavender, sage, thyme, wormwood, rosemary, tarragon, hyssop, marjoram, mint and the colourful flowers of borage, bergamot, catnip, chamomile, roses, santolina, golden rod, meadowsweet, plumbago etc.

1 Cover a wire wreath base with sphagnum moss so that the wire is completely concealed and fix it in place with fine insulating wire.

2 Cut sprigs all the same length and insert them in the wire working from left to right or right to left if you work better that way. All sprigs must face the same way. You can use them mixed or in successive groups of different herbs.

3 Bind them in place with wire. Wind wire around the stem of each sprig, cut off and insert in the wreath. Estimate length of stem and wire needed to make the best effect. Cover base.

A wreath like this looks very pretty when fresh and if kept out of too much light and in a well-ventilated spot, will keep its looks as it dries.

A GARLAND OF DRIED HERBS

To make a garland of any size, a large amount of material is needed so it is necessary to think ahead and stockpile ready for the day the garland is to be created.

Method

Gather tansy, golden rod, rosemary, chamomile, bergamot, mixed with sprigs of thyme and lavender. Small coloured glass balls, bells, ribbons and other baubles add to the decoration.

1 Tiny bunches of herbs are tied together with wire and laid horizontally on a plait of raffia, their stems hiding that of the preceding bunch and are wired into place.

2 It is a long and quite difficult process as the wiring is fiddly. Each little bunch should be as colourful as possible and the baubles used freely.

LAVENDER WATER

Lavender water in a pretty bottle with some sprigs of lavender—makes a delightful present.

Materials:
3 tsp/15 ml lavender oil
375 ml/$^1/_2$ pint surgical spirit
1 drop essential lavender oil

Mix ingredients and store in an airtight jar for 2 weeks, shaking the jar every now and then. Strain through fine muslin and bottle.

LAVENDER SOAP MARBLES

Small balls of sweet-scented soap for travelling and for guests are easily made.

Materials:
a bar of unscented good quality soft white soap
some lavender water
a touch of essential oil of lavender

1 Grate the soap finely. Heat 2$^1/_2$ tbsp/37 ml lavender water and pour over the soap. Leave for a while to let soap begin to dissolve. Stir well.

2 Add 2-3 drops essential oil of lavender and put in the blender.
3 Blend until smooth. Pour into a basin and leave until you can see the soap is beginning to dry.

4 Take out a small quantity and roll it into a ball between the palms. Continue doing this until all the soap is used. You will know best the size of the marble or ball that will be most useful. Leave balls in a warm or sunny spot to dry.
5 When the balls are almost dry, pour some lavender water containing the merest soupcon of essential oil of lavender on to the palms of the hands and roll the balls between them to give a final polish and scent.

LAVENDER VINEGAR

Lavender vinegar, dabbed on the temples and forehead, helps to ease a miserable headache

Materials:
lavender flower spikes
white vinegar
fine muslin

1 Steep flower spikes in white vinegar in a jar in a sunny spot for a week, shaking it once a day.
2 Put a fresh lot of flowers in another jar and strain the vinegar in the first jar over them and leave the new jar in a sunny place for a week, shaking it every day. Strain through fine muslin and bottle.

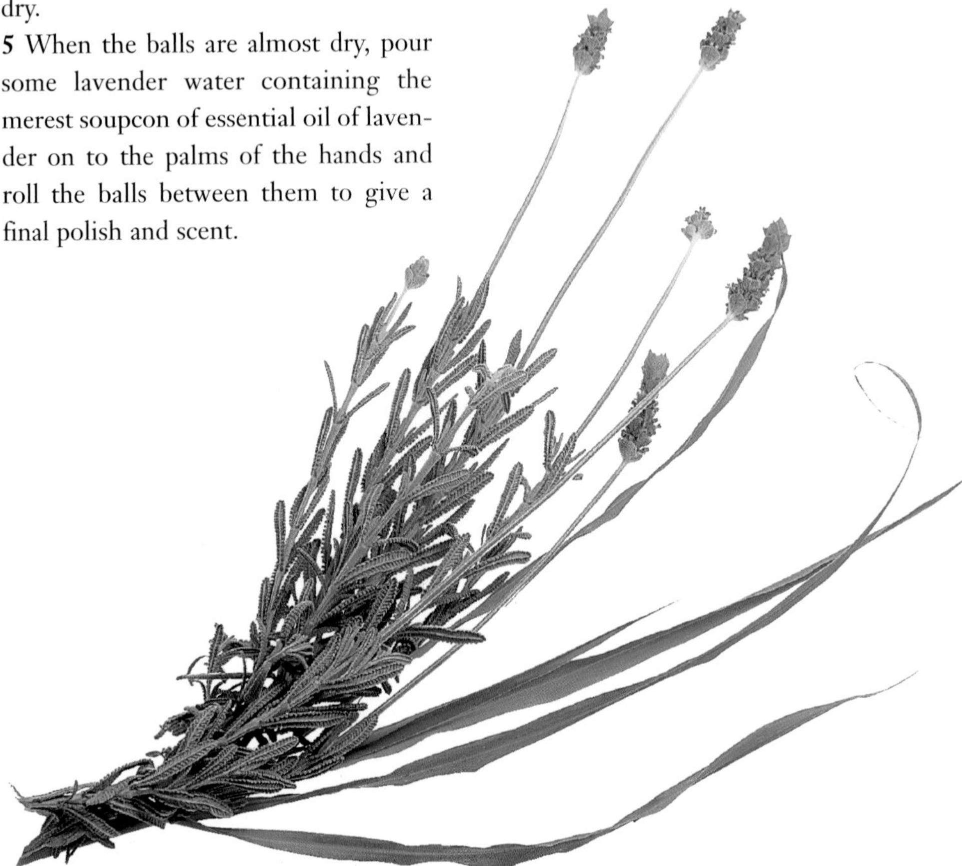

Lavender Vinegar
Lavender
Water

LAVENDER CONES

An arrangement of lavender makes a pretty, scented decorative feature.

Materials:
a large, well-opened pine-cone
short stalks of lavender flowers
a small cork
varnish
glue

1 Varnish the cone, and when dry glue it to the cork to make a base.
2 Dip the ends of the lavender stalks into the glue and push into the spaces of the opened cones. Pack the stalks in tightly and evenly.

3 When you are satisfied with the shape add a few drops of essential oil of lavender to increase the fragrance.

Instead of using the cork base you could attach ribbon to the cone and hang it by a loop in a warm room for the fragrance to be released and circulate.

LAVENDER AND HERB SACHET

Materials:
50 g/2 oz dried lavender flowers
25 g/1 oz dried lemon verbena
12 g/½ oz each of dried peppermint and dried rosemary
2 tbsp cloves, crushed
2 tbsp cinnamon stick, crushed
2 tbsp orris root powder
4 drops lavender oil
2 drops each lemon verbena and peppermint oil

1 Make sure all ingredients are dry before starting. Crumble herbs into a bowl. Be sure not to make them into dust.
2 Crush the spices and add to the bowl. Add orris root and mix everything together well.
3 Add the essential oils a drop at a time, stirring between each drop.
4 Put the mixture into a polythene bag. Seal the top and leave for six weeks to mature.
5 Fill muslin bags fairly loosely with the matured mixture so that the

Herbs and Body Care

HERBAL BATHS

There is nothing like the pleasure of a long soak in a warm bath when tension and tiredness are making us feel wretched; we emerge from the water soothed and revived. Herbs can add to our pleasure and recovery for they have properties which, released into the water, can smooth and soothe the skin, deodorise, relax the nerves or stimulate flagging energy.

BATH HERBS

Stimulating
basil, bay, fennel, lavender, lemon verbena, lovage, meadowsweet, mint, pine, rosemary, sage, thyme

Relaxing
catmint, chamomile, jasmine, lime flowers, vervain

Healing
comfrey, lady's mantle, marigold, mint, yarrow

Relieving fatigue and aching limbs
bay, bergamot, mugwort, rosemary

HERBAL BATH INFUSION

Infusions need to be concentrated as they are mixed with a large volume of water.

50 g/2 oz dried or 100 g/4 oz of fresh herbs
600 ml/l pint boiling water
jug
sieve

1 Put the herbs of your choice into the jug. add the boiling water and leave to infuse for 30 minutes.

2 Strain the infusion through the sieve and add to the bath water.

HERBAL BATH DECOCTION

This mixture contains bran to soften the water:

100 g/4 oz fresh herbs
25 g/1 oz bran
900 ml/1½ pints boiling water
stainless steel saucepan
sieve

1 Put herbs in saucepan, add water and gently bring to boil. Keep simmering until the colour of the water is quite strong. About 30 minutes.

2 Strain the mixture through the sieve and add to the bath water.

HERBAL BATH BAGS

You can also put a handful of herbs into a little muslin bag and hang the bag by a long loop to the hot tap so that the water will flow through the bag as the bath is run.

Make it a long loop so that the bag is under the water as quickly as possible—the heat of the water will release the properties of the herbs and they will be lost in the steam if the bag is left in the air.

Left: *Muslin herb bag of Lemon balm and Lavender is submerged in the bath.*
Right: *Muslin herb bags with hanging ribbons.*

A TONIC BATH

A tonic bath is good when the skin looks dingy and tired.

170 g/6 oz young blackberry shoots and leaves
560 ml/20 pints of water
saucepan
sieve

1 Combine water and blackberry leaves in saucepan and heat to 45° C/115° F
2 Infuse for about 5 minutes, strain through sieve and add to the warm bath.

Similar tonics can be made using nettle, dandelion or daisies. Allow 450 g/1 lb of dried plant to every 4 litres/8 pints of water. Allow the flowers or herbs to steep in the water for about 30 minutes. Then strain and add to the warm bath.

SKIN-SMOOTHING VINEGAR BATH

A vinegar bath soothes itchiness and aching muscles and softens the skin and the bath water. The following is enough for two baths.

300 ml/½ pint cider vinegar
300 ml/½ pint spring water
25 g/l oz dried herbs or 50 g/2 oz fresh herbs
stainless steel saucepan
bowl with cover
sieve
bottle

1 Put the cider vinegar, spring water and selected herbs into the saucepan. Heat to simmering, but do not boil.
2 Pour the mixture into a bowl and cover. Leave for 12 hours then strain and bottle.

HERBAL PROPERTIES

Deodorant herbs
basil and lovage

Tonic herbs
balm, basil, bergamot, pennyroyal, rosemary, sage

Soothing herbs
For nerves and skin: chamomile and elder flower
To relieve tension: chamomile, lemon, verbena, lime flowers, marjoram, meadowsweet, rosemary, and valerian

To ease aching limbs: bay, bergamot, hyssop, marjoram,mugwort, rosemary
.
To ease a bruised body: comfrey root and mint used together

Cosmetic herbs
For oily skin: marigold flowers, horse-tail, sage, and yarrow
For dry skin: borage, lady's mantle, mashmallow, parsley, sorrel, and violet
For aging skin: dandelion, elderflower, tansy and verbena

Astringent herbs
balm (gentle), chamomile (gentle), chervil (gentle), fennel (gentle), parsley (gentle), plantain, rosemary, sage (strong), witch hazel, yarrow (strong)

Cleansing herbs
borage, chamomile, dandelion, elder-flower, lime, lovage, nettle, plantain

Soothing herbs
balm, burdock, chamomile, coltsfoot, comfrey, elderflower, lime flowers, marigold

Healing herbs
comfrey, lady's mantle, marigold, marhmallow, mint

Antiseptic herbs
lavender, mint, thyme, witch hazel

AFTER-BATH COLOGNE

Use this fragrant cologne as a friction rub after a bath.

½ cup (250 ml) any strong scented fresh flower petals (rose, jasmine, carnation etc)
250 ml/½ cup deodorised alcohol or foodgrade isopropyl alcohol which can be obtained from most chemists
750 ml/1½ cups very hot water
3 tbsp ground citrus peel
1 tbsp dried basil or lemon verbena
1 tbsp mint or crushed thyme
cheesecloth or muslin

1 Soak flowers in the alcohol for one week in a tightly closed jar. On the sixth day, make an infusion of the peel and herbs in the hot water. Allow to stand for 24 hours.

2 Strain through cheesecloth or muslin. Drain petals. Combine the two liquids in a bottle with a screw top and shake well.

HERBAL WASHERS

To add to the effect of the bath, use this washer, pressing the bag against your body to cleans and soften the skin. Stroke arms, legs and back rhythmically and slowly.

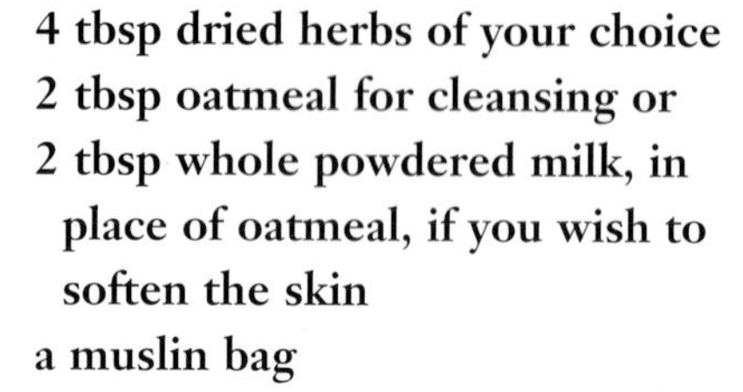

4 tbsp dried herbs of your choice
2 tbsp oatmeal for cleansing or
2 tbsp whole powdered milk, in place of oatmeal, if you wish to soften the skin
a muslin bag

1 Combine a handful of herbs of your choice with a handful of fine oatmeal.

2 Place into a muslin bag—roll it up tightly or sew it up and use as a washer.

FOOTBATH

Bathing the feet is a time-honoured restorative. A mustard foot bath will warm the whole body—a footbath containing herbs will ease it.

Horsetail is excellent for tired feet and if used regularly will reduce perspiration. Lovage is a good deodourant–lavender, sage, peppermint and thyme are instant refreshing tonics. Marjoram is soothing.

50 g/2 oz herbs
900 ml/1½ pints water
saucepan
sieve
2 tbsp sea salt

1 Boil herbs and water in a saucepan. Simmer for 30 minutes. Strain and stir in sea salt to make a decoction.

2 Add 300 ml/½ pint of the decoction to a bowl of hot water. Soak feet for 10 minutes.

STEAM BATHS

The purpose of the steam bath is to bring out deep-seated impurities and to improve the complexion by stimulating circulation. It is far more suitable for an open-pored thick oily skin than for a thin sensitive one or one where thread-veins are in evidence. It is fairly drastic treatment.

Chamomile flowers seem to please most people—comfrey, horsetail, nettle, rosemary, elderflower and lime flowers, peppermint, lady's mantle and yarrow are also used.

1 Put 1 tablespoon of dried chamomile, lime or elder flowers in a bowl and pour 300 ml/½ pint boiling water over them.
2 Lean over the steam which is rising and drape a towel over your head and the bowl to contain the hot vapour.

Don't let the steam blast directly on to your face—keep it more than 30 cm/ 12 inches away. Close your eyes and keep still while the hot steam opens the pores and the properties in the herbs released into the steam by the hot water take effect. This should not last longer than 10 minutes. Remove towel and blot face dry.
3 Splash the face with cool water to close the pores and stay indoors for a time if the weather is cold. The skin will be soft, pink and clean-looking. If it feels tight wipe it over, very gently, with moisturiser.

MOISTURISER

1 Soak some fresh or dried chamomile, lime or elder flowers, in full-cream milk overnight.
2 Strain, warm and add a little honey to the liquid and use when the honey has dissolved. Keep the remainder in a sealed bottle in the refrigerator and use before the milk begins to go off.

FACE PACKS

Face packs draw out impurities and stimulate the circulation. They suit thick oily skins better than thin dry ones.
The basis for a face pack can be fuller's earth, fine oatmeal or ground almonds if you are feeling flush. Fuller's earth looks like mud, oatmeal like porridge.

CHOOSING HERBS FOR A STEAM BATH

For an oily skin
horsetail, marigold flowers, sage, yarrow

For a dry skin
borage, lady's mantle, mashmallow, parsley, sorrel, violet

For an aging skin
dandelion, elderflower, red clover, tansy, verbena

FACE PACK FOR OILY SKIN

1 Make a cup of strong yarrow tea and allow to cool.
2 Beat up an egg white. Mix the two ingredients with enough fine oatmeal to make a paste and add a touch of cider vinegar.
3 Apply the paste to the face for no more than half an hour keeping it away from the eyes. Lie down while the paste dries. Wash the paste off with tepid water.

FACE PACK FOR DRY SKIN

1 Make a paste from fine oatmeal, a little tea made from marigold petals, a little honey, some almond, sunflower or wheatgerm oil and a beaten egg yolk.
2 Add a touch of cider vinegar and mix well. Use as described above.

CHAMOMILE CLEANSING MILK

1 Put 3 heaped tablespoons of dried chamomile flowers in a glass jar and pour 1 cup hot, not boiling, full cream milk over them.
2 Stand jar on an upturned saucer in a pan of hot water with the water reaching part way up the jar and maintain the heat over a low flame for about half an hour. The water should not boil—it is just a matter of maintaining the heat while the goodness in the herbs is being extracted into the milk.
3 Remove jar and allow the milk to become cool. Strain and store, covered, in the refrigerator. It will last about a week.

Turn down the lights and enjoy your herbal face pack.

SOOTHING CREAM

1 tbsp dried chamomile or elder flowers
almond or sunflower oil
2 tsp lanolin
1 tsp honey

1 Put flowers in a jam jar and cover with the oil.
2 Melt lanolin and pour over the mixture. Place jar on a plate in a slow oven and leave for 20 minutes or stand the jar on an upturned saucer in a saucepan containing enough hot water to come part way up the jar and keep the water simmering gently.
3 Strain, add the honey. Stir well. Pot when cool.

DAYTIME MOISTURISING CREAM

1 tsp each beeswax, lanolin and almond (or other) oil
capsule vitamin E oil
3 tsp rosewater
touch of borax

1 Melt beeswax and lanolin and stir well to combine.
2 Add warm oils gradually and beat well. Dissolve borax in warmed rosewater and beat into the mixture. Beat until cool and thickened. You can add a few drops of your favourite essential oil to give fragrance. Pot in a pretty jar.

MARIGOLD CREAM

250 ml/1 cup strong marigold petal tea
Equal quantities beeswax, lanolin and almond, sunflower or wheat germ oil— about 2 tbsp each
touch of borax powder

1 Dissolve wax, lanolin and oil and mix together. Dissolve borax in the warm tea. Working slowly and carefully, gradually pour some of each mixture into a bowl, beating and mixing as you go.
2 Continue until all ingredients are used. Keep on beating and mixing until the mixture thickens and cools. Pot.

A pot of beautiful herbal cream made with almond oil, lanolin, beeswax, dried chamomile, rosewater and honey.

HERBS FOR HAIR

Herbs for dry hair
comfrey, elderflower, marshmallow, nettle, parsley, sage

Herbs for greasy hair
balm, horsetail, lavender, marigold, rosemary, southernwood, witch-hazel, yarrow

Herbs which help with dandruff
chamomile, lavender, nettle, parsley, rosemary, southernwood, thyme

Herbs good for limp, lack-lustre hair
basil, horsetail, lime flowers, marigold flowers, rosemary, sage, southernwood

Herbs good for falling hair
catmint, marshmallow, parsley, rosemary, southernwood

Herbs good for itchy scalp
catmint, chamomile, comfrey

Herbs for setting the hair
aloe vera

SHAMPOO

Bought shampoos have accustomed us to luscious sweet-scented lather but lather has little to do with cleanliness. Soap herbs do not produce a foamy lather, just a light sudsy one.

HERBAL "SOAPS"

Soapwort *(Saponaria officinalis)*

A pretty plant with pink flowers, smooth green stems and pointed leaves. It grows wild in temperate parts of the world and cultivated varieties can be found if you ask around. It likes rich, moist soil and some shade and is a very good plant to have in the garden both for its appearance and its use. The whole plant contains saponin—when the root, leaves and stems are boiled in water they give off a light soapy lather. If you don't grow your own herb, dried soapwort is obtainable at herbalists.

Yucca (Yucca filamentosa)
the dried root is used.
Or **Soapbark *(Quillaja saponaria)***
the dried bark is used.

All you have to do is to pour hot water over a small amount of chopped herb and beat the water until suds form. Used alone the water makes a good, clean shampoo that leaves little residue on the hair. Mixed with an infusion of herbs it makes an even better one.

HERBAL SHAMPOO

1 Pour 600 ml/l pint of boiling water over a handful dried soapwort and leave, covered, to cool.
2 Meanwhile, make a strong cupful infusion of the herb most suited to your needs and leave that to cool. After about half an hour strain the soapwort and add the water to the infusion.

This makes a shampoo which is gently soapy and which conditions the hair.

If you wish to make sure all vestige of shampoo is removed, tip some cider vinegar into the final rinsing water.

If soapwort, yucca or soapbark is unobtainable, mix together equal quantities baby shampoo and a very strong "tea" made from the herb of your choice. If you plan to use all the shampoo at one go you can beat in an egg and a squeeze of fresh aloe gel to give more shine and body. Leave out the egg if you wish to store the shampoo.

DRY SHAMPOO

Mix together equal quantities orris root powder and powdered arrowroot or cornflour and fuller's earth, and sprinkle over the hair, systematically using a comb to make sure all the hair is covered. Leave for about 15 minutes for the powder to absorb grease and dirt and then brush out (not with a nylon brush) until the hair looks clean and shiny.

HAIR CONDITIONERS

Herbs can be steeped in oil and used as conditioners just as one steeps them in oil and uses them in cooking.

Put a quantity of bruised herbs suitable for your hair in a glass jar and cover them with oil—sunflower, safflower, peanut, soya—olive oil if you are brunette. Cover with muslin or other open cloth which will let air through and put the jar somewhere warm, out of direct heat and where the temperature does not drop dramatically. Leave for at least a fortnight, shaking the jar each day. Strain, pressing the herbs with a spoon to get all the oil out of them. Bottle and add a pretty label.

Oils for conditioning can be slightly warmed, rubbed through the hair and massaged into the scalp.

When the oil has been applied, put on a plastic bath cap, wrap head in a warm towel and relax in a warm place for half an hour or so. Change towel for another warm one if it cools too quickly.

LIGHT CONDITIONER

1 tbsp each lanolin, glycerine and almond oil
3 drops rosemary oil
1 egg

1 Warm and combine all ingredients except the egg. Mix.thoroughly.
2 Beat in the beaten egg.
3 Using the fingers, stroke the conditioner through the hair and massage into the scalp. Put on a bath cap and sit and enjoy a cup of tea then rinse the hair thoroughly with warm water.

RINSE FOR FAIR HAIR

Make a strong tea from a mixture of dried chamomile, marigold and lemon verbena flowers. When cool rinse through the hair several times.

A RINSE FOR DARK HAIR

1 Make a strong tea from a mixture of sage and rosemary leaves. When cool rinse through the hair several times.
2 Save the remains of a pot of Indian tea and use that as a rinse.
For red hair a tea made from marigold petals is a good rinse.

DYEING HAIR

Henna has proved down the years that it does not injure the hair though the colour it can produce when used in inexperienced hands has been known to create a great deal of dismay. Henna is for the fun-loving prepared to take a chance.

If you buy henna powder for home use, ask for instructions as to how to use it and stick to them. The colour you create will last for up to three months.

Henna is actually quite good for the hair, it adds fullness and lustre and does not attack the natural pigment. If you really want to "go henna" begin by going to a professional and learn exactly how to get it right.

Sadly, if you do use it and hate the result you will have to wait until the hennaed hair has grown out before you can safely re-dye it or have a permanent wave.

Right: *Using herbal shampoo and conditioner adds natural beauty and sheen to the hair.*

deth but one flower, of a meane ſiſe, that is neither ſo great as many others of the following Bellflowers are, nor
yet ſo ſmall as the littleneſſe of the plant might ſeeme to promiſe, of a ſullen darke purpliſh colour : the ſeede and
roote are anſwerable to the Peach leafed Bellflower, which as I ſayd is extant in my former booke, and the figure
thereof here exhibited.
The leaſt broad leafed Bellflower.
Wilde field Bellflowers.
13. Campanula linifolia cærulea.

Herbal Reference Guide

The herbs are listed under common names.

AGRIMONY (Cocklebur)

Agrimonia eupatoria

Family: Rosaceae
Parts used: roots and leaves

This tall perennial has small, yellow, lightly scented flowers hairy, sticky grey-green toothed leaves, and bristly seed-pods—hence the country name—Cocklebur. The pods contain just two seeds. Propagated from seed.

Pick the leaves for drying just before the flowers open.

Medicinal Use: astringent, de-obstruent, diuretic, tonic

The tea, made from the leaves, is rich in iron, silica and vitamins A and K and makes both a good tonic and face-wash for an open-pored, oily skin.

More importantly the tea is good for bathing ulcerated varicose veins and persistent sores.

ALOE VERA

Family: Liliaceae
Parts used: leaves

A tall perennial with thick fleshy leaves and yellow or red flowers. It needs well-drained soil and protection from extremes of weather. It can tolerate water shortage.

Propagate by division or pull off a basal shoot and plant.

Medicinal use: laxative, anthelmintic, balsamic

A dried preparation of the gel is used for constipation and to expel thread-worms.

The gel in the fleshy leaves relieves burns and sores and can act as a sun tan lotion. Snap off a leaf and apply the cut edge to the wound.

A pot of aloe kept on the kitchen window-sill is a handy first aid for burns and scalds.

Eczema has been found to respond to frequent applications of the fresh gel.

ANGELICA (Lungwort)

Angelica archangelica

Family: Umbelliferae
Parts used: root, seeds and herb

This tall biennial has hollow stems, glossy leaves and umbels of white-yellow sweetly scented flowers.

It grows happily in both sun and light shade provided the soil is good and well-drained but able to retain moisture. It self-seeds easily. If growing from seed, transplant when the little plants are around 7.5 cm/3 inches high, and give them plenty of room. They will make big plants. Keep a few spare ones on hand as they do not transplant very well.

The leaves should be gathered for drying, with the seeds, at the end of summer.

Angelica has a distinctive flavour—fresh, lightly sweet with hints of celery and aniseed.

Culinary use: The stems and dried root can be treated as a vegetable. The slightly bitter leaves are sometimes served with fish. The seeds are used to flavour liqueur. Eating the candied stems is said to create a dislike for intoxicants.

Medicinal use: stimulant, carminative, diuretic, tonic

Tea made from any part of the plant is a tonic for colds and will bring on perspiration. Chewing the stalk will relieve stomach wind. Tea made from the dried root is a tonic.

Cosmetic and household use: The leaves are used in potpourri and, fresh or dried, in the bath.

ARNICA (Leopard's bane)

Arnica montana

Family: Compositae
Parts used: roots and flowers

This medium-sized perennial with yellowish lightly scented flowers which grow on stalks rising from a rosette of ground-high leaves has hairy seeds and is a poisonous plant but one widely used medicinally. Bees love it. It likes sun and a light soil, rich in humus. Poisonous.

Propagated by seeds, root division or cuttings.

Medicinal use: wound herb
Tincture made from the flowers and root applied locally relieves the pain of bruises and sprains. Arnica ointment and arnica in homeopathic dosage are good to have on hand as first-aids, particularly if there are children around.

BALM OR LEMON BALM

(Bee herb, Honey plant)
Melissa officinalis

Family: Labiatae
Parts used: leaves

Balm is a medium-sized, hardy, spreading perennial which is best grown in a poorish, light soil as it rampages in a moist rich one. It will take sun or shade. The leaves are small, crinkled and lemon-scented, the flowers small and pale.

Bees love balm. Beekeepers rub their hives with its crushed leaves so as to increase the colony. Propagated by seed or division.

The leaves are cut for drying just before the flowers come out. Fresh ones, wrapped in foil, will keep in the refrigerator for a week or so.

Medicinal use: carminative, febrifuge, sedative
Tea made from the leaves is light and lemony in taste and is comforting when one has a cold. Any left in the pot can be

used as a mouthwash.

It is also good for low blood pressure, menstrual cramps and troubled digestion.

In the home a strong pot of tea makes a pleasant addition to the bath water. When dried the leaves hold their fragrance well and are popular for potpourri.

BASIL
Ocimum basilicum

Family: Labiatae
Parts used: leaves

In hot climates basil can be grown as a perennial—in cooler ones it is better treated as an annual.

The plants, about 50 cm/20 inches high, have sweet-smelling leaves of different colours according to type, and purplish-white flowers which grow in spikes. Bees love it. Propagated by seed.

The herb grows wild in hot, humid regions, and cultivated extensively in numerous forms.

Sow under glass in spring or or outside after after the frosts are finished.

When the seedlings are growing well, pinch out the growing tips to help the plant become bushy.

Pick leaves for drying just before flowers come out. A pot of basil on the window-sill will deter flies and plants grown near tomatoes will help the fruit to resist disease.

Culinary use: The leaves, fresh or dried, flavour any savoury dish but have a special affinity with the tomato.

Basil is, of course, the basis of the famous Pesto sauce.

Medicinal use: Snuff made from the powdered leaves clears the sinuses.
Tea made from 5 g/1 tsp leaves and flowering tips to a cup of boiling water settles the nerves and is said to help with headaches, soothe pain and treat vomiting.

BAY (Laurel)
Laurus nobilis

Family: Lauraceae
Parts used: leaves and berries

Bay is a handsome shrub which can grow into a small tree about 9 m/30 feet high. It has dark green, shiny, tough leaves with a distinctive scent. It should be planted in well-drained soil in a sunny spot in Spring or Autumn.

Propagation can be made from cuttings but they take a long time to come to much. Most people buy a plant.

Household use: The leaves, which are very popular as a food flavouring, can be picked and used at any time of the year. They dry very well and keep their aroma and so are popular in dried arrangements and for adding to potpourri.

A few leaves in containers of farinaceous foods will keep weevils away.

Medicinal use: diuretic
Tea made from the leaves rids the body of excess water and eases the misery of a hang-over.

BERGAMOT (Bee balm. Oswego tea)
Monarda didyma

Family: Labiatae
Parts used: leaves and flowers

This tall perennial with soft green leaves and a whorl of scented red flowers, makes a good border plant which spreads well, but it needs to be dug up, the roots tidied and then replanted every few years for it to stay at its best. Bees seek out bergamot for the nectar in the lovely flower throats.

Propagate from seed, spring cuttings or root division.

Flowers and leaves are picked for drying in high summer when the plant is at its best. Both flowers and leaves dry well. and are good for potpourri.

Culinary use: The young leaves and flowers are used in salads, fruit drinks and in pork dishes. Boiling milk poured over a dessertspoonful of dried leaves makes a good nightcap.

Medicinal use: The leaves contain thymol, a powerful antiseptic oil. An infusion makes a good gargle for a sore throat.

BORAGE (Bee bread)
Borago officinalis

Family: Boraginaceae
Parts used: stems, leaves and flowers

This medium-size annual with crinkled hairy leaves and clusters of blue star-shaped flowers likes sun and will self-seed generously even in poor soil. The intense blue of the flowers is very attractive. The plant however, tends to flop. Bees love it—hence the country name.

The leaves and flowers can be picked, for use fresh, at any time. The roots used to flavour wine. and young leaves added to salads for flavour. It is also included in some drinks as a reviver.

The dried leaves and flowers add colour and fragrance to potpourri.

Culinary use: The cucumber-tasting leaves are good in salads and summer fruit drinks and make a nice tea, particularly when mixed with basil. The pretty blue flowers are used to decorate a salad when fresh; candied they are used to decorate cakes and trifles.

Medicinal use: demulcent, stimulant, diuretic

The plant is rich in potassium and calcium. An infusion made from leaves and flowers makes a good tonic, blood cleanser, laxative and cough soother. It is also said to increase the flow of adrenaline—which is probably why the ancients claimed that it "driveth away all sadness".

CATMINT(Catnip)
Nepeta cataria

Family: Labiatae
Parts used: leaves and flowers

This medium sized perennial has grey-green leaves and blue-grey flowers which grow in whorls. It likes a light, well-drained soil and sun, but will take some shade. It makes a lovely border plant provided it is controlled.

Propagating from cuttings is easy but division is quicker.

The bruised leaves and flowers give off a fragrance which cats love and given half a chance they will roll in it and flatten the plant, so don't plant it near any precious plants. Rats hate it. Bees love it.

Cut back hard after flowering it will bloom again.

Medicinal use: carminative, diaphoretic, tonic

The bruised, fresh leaves reduce the inflammation of piles.

Tea made from the leaves and flowers brings on perspiration .

It eases colds and chills, relieves neuralgia, stomach cramps and hiccups, helps to bring on delayed menstruation.

Cosmetic use: The leaves and flowers simmered in water make a rinse which will darken mousy hair.

CHAMOMILE
German chamomile
(Matricaria recutita)
Roman chamomile
(Anthemis nobilis)

Family: Compositae
Parts used: flowers and herb

The German variety is a medium-sized annual which grows wild by the wayside and self-seeds freely. In the garden it makes a small, compact, bushy plant.

The Roman (or English) is a low-growing creeping perennial with strong runners which form a mat and which can be mowed like a grass lawn. It is more strongly scented than the German variety. There is a non-flowering variety even more suitable for a lawn—the Treneague strain.

Both types have feathery leaves and small white daisy type flowers. The yellow centre of the Roman chamomile flower is hollow.

Both varieties like a moist well-drained soil, and sunshine.

The seed is very tiny and it is less trouble to propagate from offshoots.

The flowers should be gathered when they are fully opened but before the sun has become hot. Frequent picking will encourage the plant to continue flowering.

Medicinal use: sedative, antiseptic

Tea made from the flowers is a well-known soother for both the nerves and the digestion. Chamomile flowers added to a hot bath before bed help to ensure relaxed sleep.

The flowers, soaked in hot water, make a good poultice for boils etc and comfort rheumaticky joints.

Cosmetic use: A strong infusion of dried or fresh flowers keeps blonde hair blonde.

CHERVIL (Poor man's tarragon)
Anthriscus cerefolium

Family: Umbelliferae
Parts used: leaves

Chervil is a delicate little annual about 30 cm/12 inches high with feathery, light-green leaves and umbels of tiny white flowers.

It needs a good, moist soil, filtered sun and very gentle handling. Sow seed where the plants are to grow and thin out. Do not attempt to transplant any seedlings. Keep seedlings sheltered from hot sun, cold draughts and wind. Be sure to water regularly.

Growing it in a container makes looking after it easier. It doesn't dry well but is a nice little herb to have around.

Culinary use: The leaves have a light aniseed flavour which makes them very pleasant in a salad or as a finely chopped garnish for food. They are used with parsley, chives and tarragon to make a bouquet garni. Alone they go with any savoury dish.

Don't bother to dry chervil—pick it and use it fresh throughout the season.

Medicinal use: tonic
Chervil is one of the traditional "spring" herbs. An infusion purifies the blood, is a tonic for nerves and brain, and is said to help a failing memory and to lower high blood pressure. If buying a plant ask for it by its botanical name to avoid confusion with other chervils.

CHICKWEED
Stellaria media

Family: Caryophyllaceae
Parts used: Whole plant

Every gardener must know this little annual weed which appears year after year without any encouragement, It is tiny, low-growing with succulent stems and white flowers like little stars.

It pulls up very easily and if you take it straight to your caged bird you will have made his day for chickweed tastes good and is rich in iron and copper.

Medicinal use: tonic, demulcent

An infusion of the stems and leaves makes a slightly salty tasting tonic tea. Strain any left and use as a bath for sore eyes.

Skin conditions difficult to cure, have been known to respond to a poultice of fresh stems and leaves. The poultice is said to ease arthritis and pain of the joints. It is used in a homeopathic remedy for rheumatism.

CHICORY
Cichorum intybus

Family: Compositae
Part used: root, flowering stems, seeds

Chicory is a tallish perennial with stems up to 1.5 m/5 ft which needs light soil and a sunny, open position. The stem is hollow, furrowed and hairy and contains a bitter juice.

The lower leaves are large, long, pointed and toothy and the ones higher on the stem are small and grow on a myriad of stalks which carry pale blue flowers in the axils of the leaves. The flowers open and close regularly. Wherever chicory grows the leaves always align with the south.

Sow early in the year where you want the plants to grow. Thin but do not transplant.

Pick leaves when young. Dig up roots in autumn.

Culinary use: The leaves are bitter and to make them acceptable as a vegetable or a salad they have to be blanched, by covering the plant with a layer of sand. That is the simple way.

A more troublesome one is to lift growing plants in the autumn, strip off the leaves and pack them together, upright, under a layer of sandy soil in a big box and keep them in a dark place watering them regularly. When the leaves come out they will be very pale—blanched—and you will no doubt recognise them as those of the plant sold in the markets as Witloof.

Medicinal use: The roots which can grow quite large can be dried, roasted and ground and made into a drink which is good for the liver and digestion.

Chicory tea is used to stimulate bile secretion and to treat gout, rheumatism, anaemia and liver complaints.

Caution: Excessive use can can lead to digestive upsets. Handling may cause dermatitis in some people.

CHIVES
Allium schoenoprasum and allium tuberosum

Family: Liliaceae
Parts used: leaves

Chives are the babies of the onion family but are grown for their leaves rather than their bulbs. They are perennials, and grow in clusters. Their fine upright leaves and pretty pink pom-pom flowers make them an attractive border-edging plan and they have excellent culinary and medical properties.

They like warm, moist soil and sun and dislike being chilled. Propagate by division.

The garlic-flavoured variety makes a good edging for a rose bed as it gives protection against aphids.

Nip the flowers out if the leaves are wanted for the kitchen, if you don't the leaves will be tough. Keeping the leaves well-picked will encourage growth.

Culinary use: The leaves can be kept in the freezer, wrapped in foil, until wanted for use in cooking. They won't do for salads as they become limp when defrosted. Leaves for salads can be kept for a time, wrapped in foil, in the refrigerator.

Chopped chives go with practically everything savoury. Because, like onions, they contain sulphur, they are good for health.

In the garden: A border of chives round the rose-bed will deter aphids.

COLTSFOOT (Coughwort)
Tussilago farfara

Family: Compositae
Parts used: flowers and leaves

Coltsfoot is a perennial weed which grows in any soil in temperate areas.

It grows to about 1 cm /½in high and has broad, hoof-shaped woolly leaves and yellow daisy-like flowers which die before the leaves come out and turn into seeds which can be puffed away like dandelion clocks.

Propagation although seldom necessary as they self-seed well is by division.

Medicinal use: demulcent, expectorant
The dried leaves form the greatest part of herbal tobacco. An old asthma remedy was to throw a quantity of leaves on to a dried wood fire and to inhale the smoke.

A herbal tea made from the leaves to ease a raspy throat, should be strained well to make sure all the downy hairs are removed. Any tea left can be used as a face wash to minimise thread-veins.

COMFREY (Knitbone, Boneset)
Symphytum officinale

Family: Boraginaceae
Parts used: leaves and roots

A tall perennial with hollow, hairy stems bearing large, hairy pointed leaves which decrease in size from the bottom of the stem upward, Bluish, yellowish or whitish flowers grow in spikes at the top of the stems. The plant is tall, broad and grows strongly and so needs plenty of space. It flourishes in all temperate areas if given good moist soil and some shade. Propagate by root division.

Medicinal use: demulcent, astringent, pectoral, styptic, vulnerary

Its wonderful reputation rests on its ability to knit together broken bones and torn flesh. Wounds, burns and scalds heal without leaving a scar if treated promptly with a poultice made from the leaves.

The plant contains allantoin which encourages the healthy granulation of tissue both inside and outside the body and for a long time it was accepted that the liquid from the chopped root (150 g/ 5 oz soaked in a litre of water) was beneficial in the treatment of stomach ulcers. Its use internally is now discouraged—many people think the reasons given do not carry sufficient weight to justify the stricture.

In the garden: Comfrey improves strawberries grown nearby. The leaves make an excellent compost activator or liquid fertiliser.

Cosmetic use: A steam-bath made from the leaves will revitalise tired skin.

CORIANDER
Coriandrum sativum

Family: Umbelliferae
Parts used: leaves and seed

Coriander is a medium-sized annual with parsley-like leaves and umbels of pinkish flowers. It needs good, friable soil and plenty of sun to ensure healthy growth.

Culinary use: Both leaves and seeds are used for flavouring salads, cakes, stewed fruit, pork and ham dishes.

The leaves may be picked fresh for use at any time. They will keep rolled in foil in the freezer.

Pick the flowerheads when the seeds are ripe and the head about to fall. Dry in the shade. Remove all the flower bits and sieve before storing.

COSTMARY (Alecost)
Tanacetum balsamita

Family: Compositae
Parts used: leaves

This tallish perennial has long, narrow, pale leaves and button-like yellow flowers and a minty, slightly bitter scent and grows to 60 cm/2 ft. It likes temperate areas, full sun and good, well-drained soil. The roots spread quickly so the plant needs plenty of space. Propagate by root division.

Medicinal use: astringent, antiseptic Crushed fresh leaves relieve the sting of insect bites. Tea made from the leaves makes a pleasant tonic drink.

COWSLIP (Paigles, Our Lady's keys)
Primula veris

Family: Primulaceae
Parts used: flowers and leaves

One of the best-loved English wild flowers, the cowslip grows in hedgerows and woods in early Spring. The creamy-yellow flowers, which have a delicate fragrance rise on slender stems from low-growing downy leaves. It makes a lovely addition to the informal parts of the garden.

Culinary use: The fresh flowers make a sweet salad garnish but are disappointing in taste when dried.

Medicinal use: Tea made from the flowers and leaves is laxative and diuretic but must be well-sieved to prevent its tiny hairs irritating the stomach.

Cosmetic use: A face wash of cowslip tea was said to "take away spots and wrinkles and add beauty exceedingly".

Wine made from the flowers used to be a well-known—and potent—country drink.

DANDELION (Piss-a-bed)
Taraxacum officinalis

Family: Compositae
Parts used: leaves, roots and flowers

This is one of the richest plants in the whole plant kingdom, It contains iron, copper, inulin, protein and a range of vitamins and mineral salts.

The dandelion has a low, clumped growth with a rosette of dark green, toothed leaves at its base. Shaggy, brilliant flowers are held erect on hollow stalks. The deep tap root, leaves and stem contain a milky juice. It will grow anywhere but glories in the sun.

A patch of dandelions in the garden gives young leaves for salads and tonic drinks, flowers for wine-making and roots for drying for making into a coffee substitute. The roots are harvested in the autumn of its second growing season.

Medicinal use: digestive, diuretic, tonic This favourite medical herb is said to be able to reduce the amount of sugar in the blood, and so be of aid to diabetics. It also reduces high blood pressure and removes excess water from the body.

A simple spring cure which rids the blood of impurities by stimulating the flow of urine and bile, is made by boiling 1 tablespoonful of fresh, cleaned, chopped root in half a cup of water and drinking when cool. It should be made fresh, and taken twice a day for a day or two.

The milky juice of the plant is used to remove warts and corns.

Cosmetic use: The water in which young flowers have been boiled makes a good skin cleanser and is said to remove freckles.

DILL
Anethum graveolens

Family: Umbelliferae
Parts used: leaves and seeds

Dill is an annual plant with blue-green feathery leaves, a speckled smooth stem and umbels of small yellow flowers. It grows easily from seed, self-sows readily but does not transplant well.

The plants can grow to a metre high but the stems are delicate so it is wise to give protection against wind and stake if necessary. They require sun and a light well-drained soil and careful attention as they will die if allowed to dry out.

Bees like it—the white cabbage moth doesn't.

The seeds ripen in autumn when they can be picked for drying.

The leaves should be picked, for use fresh or for drying, before the flowers come out—this ensures the aniseed flavour is strong.

Culinary use: Dill seeds gives flavour to soups, sauces, salads and cheese.

Medicinal use: Dill water is a well-known mother's friend—the bought product called Gripewater soothed countless babies in past years.

An infusion made from the leaves and seeds tastes nice and will soothe an upset stomach and ease hiccups. Nursing mothers may prefer an infusion made with wine—this is good for stimulating the production of milk.

ELDER
Sambucus nigra

Family: Caprifoliaceae
Parts used: bark, flowers and leaves

Elder makes a big shrub or a small tree—if you can cope with its height (6-7 m/19-22 ft). It is good to have around because flowers, berries and bark are all useful. The fissured bark can be soft grey to mid-brown and the dark green toothed leaves have a scent as unpleasant and strong as that of the clusters of creamy flowers is light and sweet. The flowers are followed by black berries.

Given adequate sun and moisture elders tolerate any type of soil. If you don't have room in the wilder part of the garden you might consider growing one in a large container.

The roots give off a substance which aids fermentation so elder is a good plant to use to hide the compost heap. The flowers should be picked for drying when they are in full bloom.

Culinary use: Champagne can be made from the flowers and syrup from the berries. The one will gladden the heart, the other reduce a heavy cold and clear blocked sinuses.

Medicinal use: alterative, diuretic, febrifuge, sudorific

Elderflower tea brings on perspiration and will "break" a heavy cold. So will syrup made from the berries. Weak tea makes a good eye-wash. Ointment made from the leaves soothes minor wounds and scrapes.

A small branch kept in the kitchen will keep flies out and a leaf rubbed over the skin while gardening will give protection against insects.

ELECAMPANE (Scabwort)
Inula helenium

Family: Compositae
Parts used: root

This tall perennial has large tapering leaves which are hairy underneath and shaggy yellow flowers. It needs a moist, semi-shady spot with good soil. It is mostly grown for its root which, when chewed, is said to be the best possible thing for indigestion.

The flowers are quite handsome in dried arrangements.

Propagation is made by root division.

EVENING PRIMROSE
Oenothera biennis

Family: Onagraceae
Parts used: leaves and stem

This tall, biennial has low-growing leaves and papery, sweetly scented yellow flowers growing in spikes. It likes temperate conditions with sun and a light, well-drained soil which its tap root penetrate easily. It grows readily from seed and self-seeds well.

Medicinal use: astringent, sedative

An infusion of leaves and stems, well-strained, is a gentle sedative and is also useful in cases of whooping cough and asthma.

EYEBRIGHT
Euphrasia officinalis

Family: Scrophulariacceae
Part used: whole plant

This bushy little annual has toothed, slightly hairy leaves and pinky-white lobed flowers which have yellow spots and carry a thin red line on the lower lobe. It grows well in poor soil and dry places provided it is near grass so that it can leach nourishment from its roots. It is well worth having in the garden just for its medicinal use.

Medicinal use: astringent, tonic
The fresh juice of the plant or an infusion made from it has long been used for sore eyes and dim sight. Eyebright tea is said to assist children who are slow learners. Sufferers from hay-fever should drink it when the pollen count is high.

FENNEL
Foeniculum vulgare

Family: Umbelliferae
Parts used: stem, seeds, leaves and root

There are many varieties of fennel—the most popular is the Florentine which is an annual plant with a fat, swollen leaf-base; the Italian variety has straight, tender stems and is often confused with dill. Florentine fennel grows to about 2 m/6 feet, high, has bright green feathery leaves with an aniseed scent and round, ribbed, smooth shiny stems. The handsome yellow flowers grow in umbels. Although it is unfriendly to most other herbs it makes a good back-of-the flower border plant.

It likes a well-drained soil, sun or part shade. It grows easily from seed but the seedlings do not transplant well so it is quicker and safer to increase stock by root division. The seedheads should be removed for drying in the autumn.

Culinary use: The leaves do not dry too well so it is best to keep foil-wrapped packets of them in the freezer.
The chopped leaves and stems make a refreshing addition to salads—snipped-up leaves add flavour to sauces and home-made cottage cheese. The seeds, sprinkled on plain scones before cooking, give them an aniseed flavour.

Medicinal use: carminative, stimulant, stomachic

A few chewed seeds sweeten the breath and help digestion.

Fennel seed tea is good for flatulence, for bathing sore eyes relieving headaches, blocked sinuses, torpid livers and the pain of gout, rheumatism, insect and snake bites. It used to be so well thought of it was believed to give protection against witches and ghosts. It certainly gives dogs protection against fleas.

A few sprigs kept in the kennel and a bunch, crushed in the hand until the juices flow and then rubbed into his coat, will make a dog very happy for all dogs seem to love the smell and taste of fennel.

It is rich in iron, potassium, and vitamins A and C and is low in kilojoules. It is called the slimmer's herb.

FENUGREEK (Bird's foot)
Trigonella foenum-graceum

Family: Leguminaceae
Parts used: seeds

Fenugreek is a member of the pea and bean family and is a tallish annual with clover-like leaves, scented cream, yellow or pink flowers and bean-shaped seeds. It likes temperate conditions, sun and a good soil.

Fenugreek has mainly been used as cattle feed and an ingredient of curry powder but the sprouted seeds, which contain calcium and vitamins are being increasingly used for sprouting for use in salads. Their flavour goes well with mashed potatoes.

Medicinal use: febrifuge, tonic
A seed tea helps the digestion, reduces fever, increases lactation and is said to shorten the duration of a migraine headache.

A seed poultice will "draw" boils and soften corns.

FEVERFEW (Featherfoil)
Tanecetum parthenium

Family: Compositae
Parts used: leaves and stems

Feverfew makes a small perennial clump of yellow-green feathery, serrated leaves and pretty daisy-like flowers, sometimes double and stems up to 90 cm/3 ft.. It needs sun and dryish conditions. Propagation is by seed, cuttings or root division.

The flowers and leaves can be picked at any time for use fresh or for drying. The dried flowers are used in potpourri, the dried leaves as a moth deterrent.

Medicinal use: emmenogoguic, laxative, nervine, tonic, vermifuge

Tea made from the leaves is a mild disinfectant and laxative, will quieten screaming nerves, promote the senses and expel worms.

Migraine sufferers find benefit from chewing a few leaves every day. Since the taste is bitter, it can be disguised by making them into a sandwich. This is not claimed to be a cure but tests have proved that most people find some relief.

It has long been used as a tonic and to treat indigestion. Leaves are made into pain killing poultices for limb and joint aches.

Caution: fresh leaves may cause mouth ulcers.

FLAX (Linseed)
Linum usitatissimum

Family: Linaceae
Parts used: stems and seeds

Flax is a medium-sized hardy annual with small grey-green leaves and flowers of a deep, pure blue. The shiny light brown seeds contain the linseed oil so well known to both artist and housewife. Flax likes sun and a dryish open position. The capsules containing the seeds should be gathered when the seeds are ripe and before the capsules fall.

Culinary use: The seeds, rich in calcium and iron, are tasty when sprouted.

Medicinal use: Raw seeds, once popular as a laxative,are less so now as they have been found to irritate the intestines. They should not be taken by expectant mothers.

Tea made from the seeds is good for bad chests and the soaked seeds for making a poultice to "draw" boils.

Household use: A splendid furniture polish is made by using equal quantities of linseed oil and turpentine mixed with a third the quantity of both vinegar and methylated spirits.

FOXGLOVE (Fairy thimbles, Dead mens' helmets)
Digitalis purpurea

Family: Scrophulariaceae
Parts used: leaves

Foxglove is a poisonous plant so, if you have children, you might think twice about having it in the garden.

It is a tall biennial with green hairy leaves and spikes of tubular white, pink or purple flowers. It likes shade and can take some dryness. It is a decorative border plant which self-seeds well.

Oddly enough it is an antidote to aconite poisoning so if you have both plants in the garden you have some protection.

The poison is inactive in the soil so spent plants can be safely added to the compost heap.

Medicinal use: cardiac, diuretic

The leaves contain digitalis which is a well-known medicine for heart disease and blood pressure, but the gardener should NEVER be tempted to make his own medicine from them. Digitalis is a substance that should only be taken under medical supervision.

GARLIC

Allium sativum

Family: Liliaceae
Part used: bulb

Garlic has been grown all over the world for centuries, providing both food, medicine and protection against disease. The builders of the Gizeh and the Cheops pyramids ate it in great quantities and so did the Roman legions.

A garlic bulb is round and made up of 10 to 20 cloves, each one of which, when separated, will produce a plant. The bulb is wrapped in a papery skin.

The plant is a perennial which can grow quite tall. The flat, long grey-blue leaves arch and droop; round heads of pinkish-white flowers rise on erect stems. Garlic likes a well-drained, rich soil and plenty of sunshine but is good-tempered enough to take partial shade.

The whole plant carries a lingering, invasive odour.

If you separate a bulb of garlic, the cloves can be planted individually in drills, 15 cm/6 inches apart and 4 cm/2 inches deep, or around rose-beds—or where you will. Garlic is a good companion to most plants.

The flowers should be cut early to encourage the bulbs to fatten. When the leaves turn brown in autumn you can dig up the plant and dry it or separate the bulb into cloves and immediately replant.

Culinary use: Meat, fish, vegetables, salads, stews all take on life and flavour given the addition of crushed garlic.

Unfortunately a blast of garlic-laden breath has been known to destroy romance. A sprig of parsley, well-chewed, will save the day. Soaking the cloves in water for a few hours before use will reduce the smell but not the taste.

Medicinal use: antiseptic, antispasmodic, carminative, diaphoretic, diuretic, expectorant, stomachic, vermifuge

Garlic is often considered the first line of defence in the preservation of health. It is a wonderful disinfectant and antiseptic.

As a quick first aid press a cut clove against a wound. Rub one over a corn to loosen it. Make a poultice of the cloves and use when sores are slow to heal.

Boiling milk poured over a few cloves of garlic makes a drink which will ease an upset stomach, keep down high blood pressure and help sufferers from arterio-sclerosis.

A whole bulb of garlic, crushed and mixed into a small jar of vaseline and left for a week in a warm place, makes a good rub for tight chests.

A syrup made from garlic juice and honey will help to reduce bronchial and catarrhal mucus. If the smell proves too much—and it is for most people—garlic perles which have no noticeable odour can be bought commercially.

Rub fresh cloves on acne, or mash and use on warts or to draw corns.

In the garden: Insects such as aphids, red spiders and scale insects do not like its smell, so garlic gives plants growing nearby protection. Plant under apple trees to protect them against scale, and under peach trees to protect them against leaf curl.

A clove of garlic rubbed on the skin will give working gardeners protection against mosquitoes and pots of it on the window-sill will keep them out of the kitchen.

GENTIAN

Gentiana lutea

Family: Gentiana lutea
Parts used: roots and leaves

In medieval times, gentian was an ingredient of the alchemical brew *theriac*, a cure-all made to a highly secret recipe. The herb reputedly takes its name from a king who discovered its ability to reduce fevers.

The yellow variety is the best-known of the family, it is a perennial plant which, though slow to flower, can live for a long time. The shiny, 5-veined leaves grow opposite each other on the tall stem and the yellow, many-stemmed flowers grow from the leaf axils. The root, which is the important part of the plant, is thick and fleshy and can be huge—around a metre in length.

Although a handsome plant, it takes so long to flower that gardeners seldom bother with it. It likes the cooler areas of the world, sun or part shade and a moist soil full of leaf-mould.

The seed will only germinate in the cold so it is obviously useless to attempt to grow it in a warm climate. Root cuttings are a better bet anywhere.

If you can grow it, the roots should be collected and powdered at the beginning of autumn.

Medicinal use: anthelmintic, antiseptic, stomachic, tonic

Its powerful tonic properties have been recognised for a couple of centuries. The plant secretes a chemical that stimulates the production of stomach acid and is good taken — under medical supervision —for the digestion. It is good for poor circulation, anaemia, impure blood, suppressed menstruation. chills, fevers, liver and spleen complaints and the expulsion of worms from the body. Since it is so powerful it should not be taken by pregnant women or anyone with high blood pressure.

Caution: Gentian should only be taken under professional supervision.

GERANIUM
Pelargonium

Family: Geraniaceae
Parts used: leaves

Every garden should have a few of the scented-leaved geraniums for, although their culinary use is limited, the leaves make an invaluable addition to pot pourri, scented sachets and herb pillows.

The varieties include almond *(P. quercifolium)*, apple *(P. odoratissimum)*, apricot *(P. scabrum)*, coconut, lemon *(P. crispum)*, lime *(P. nervosum)*, nutmeg *(P. fragrans)*, peppermint *(P. tomentosum)* and the popular rose *(P. graveolens)*.

They all make fine bushy plants with insignificant flowers and are usually planted where their leaves can be brushed in passing and their scent released. The leaves vary in shape from feathery to large and rounded; and in colour from light to dark green. Some are variegated.

Propagation can be made from stem and root cuttings.

Pick leaves for drying at any time.

Culinary use: The scented leaves can be used fresh in puddings, cakes, jellies, stewed fruit and as an addition to egg custard and cottage cheese.

GERMANDER
Teucrium

Family: Labiateae
Parts used: whole plant

Germander grows wild in Europe and was once much used as a medicinal plant. There are several different varieties ranging from the prostrate to the tall and bushy and they all have attractive leaves and flowers and make good garden plants. Wall germander *(teucrium chamaedrys)* makes a pleasant border-edging and the prostrate variety a good groundcover.

The leaves, mostly shiny, oval and scalloped, vary in colour from light to dark green. The flowers are white or purple. The sage-leaved variety has greenish-yellow flowers and leaves which smell like beer.

Germander likes temperate conditions, a little shade and an acid soil but will grow almost anywhere provided the soil does not puddle.

Propagation can be made from seed, stem cuttings or root division.

The leaves should be gathered for drying just before the flowers come out.

Medicinal use: diaphoretic, diuretic, stimulant, tonic

The sage-leaved germander, often called wood sage, is a bitter, tonic herb. Tea made from the leaves will cleanse the blood, rid the body of excess water, promote menstruation, reduce fever and generally tone up the system.

GINGER
Zingiber officinale

Family: Zingiberaceae
Parts used: roots

Ginger is a tall, tropical, perennial plant which grows from large creeping rhizomes which put up bright green, broad, flat, tapering leaves. The flowers are yellow or white with purple lips.

Although it is a native of hot and humid areas it will grow in more temperate ones if given plenty of water. A small piece of bought root set in a pot just below the surface of some rich, well-drained soil will, if kept well-watered and protected against cold wind and weather, make a handsome plant. It will need regular spraying to keep it healthy. The root to use is not the one which is dried and brown and found in greengrocer shops, but a young one with a pale green skin, sold in some plant nurseries or Asian speciality shops.

Propagation is by root division. A root from the garden is not ready for drying until it is over a year old.

Culinary use: The ground root is readily available commercially. It has a sweet, hot flavour and is used in sweet dishes, cakes and biscuits. Gingerbread biscuits and gingerbread men have delighted children for many, many years. Ginger root preserved in syrup is delicious.

Ginger beer is simple to make and good for parties for the young. Whisky, with the addition of some bruised ginger root and some sugar and raisins is good for the grown-ups.

The root is widely used in Chinese, Indian and Thai cooking.

Medicinal use: carminative, expectorant, stimulant

Ginger tea made from 2 teaspoons of ginger powder to a cup of hot water and sweetened with honey or sugar is known to ease menstrual cramps, morning sickness, flatulence, chills, retention of urine. Since ginger contains sulphur it will purify the blood.

It is used with other herbs to release phlegm gathered on the chest.

It has antiseptic properties and these, with the sulphur it contains, makes it an antidote against infections.

Two tablespoonsful of powdered ginger in the bath will bring on perspiration.

GINSENG (Life Root)
Panax

Family: Araliaceae
Parts used: root

Ginseng is not a plant for the home gardener. It is tricky to grow and even more so to propagate. *P. schinseng* is the variety grown in China—*P. quinquefolium*, the one grown in North America. So much is used in China that the cultivated American variety has to be imported.

P. quinquefolium is a hardy perennial about 50 cm/20 inches high. A single stem carries 5-lobed leaves which are toothed and oval, and greenish-white flowers which grow in an umbel. They are followed by red berries. The root is large, fleshy and yellowish-brown.

Ginseng likes shade and a rich organic soil. It can be grown from seed but the process is lengthy and success doubtful.

Medicinal use: demulcent, febrifuge, stimulant, stomachic, tonic

The Chinese take it regularly and believe it gives protection against any disease. It is known to stimulate the appetite and the central nervous system, to ease an upset stomach, an inflamed bladder, constipation, a high cholesterol level and nervous and emotional strain.

Taken in a hot drink it will break a cold and comfort a cough. It can also be a gentle aphrodisiac.

GOLDEN ROD

Solidago virgaurea

Family: Compositae
Parts used: flowers and leaves

This tall perennial plant grows about a metre high, has an angular stem, narrow tapering leaves and golden-yellow flowers which grow in loosely-branched clusters at the top of the stem.

It likes the sun and will tolerate a poor soil as long as it does not get soggy, but a rich soil kept well fed and watered will suit it far better. A handsome plant in the wild it was introduced into gardens in the temperate parts of the world where it was prized for its many good properties.

Propagation is by seed or root division. The leaves and the flowering tips are gathered for drying as the flowers come out.

Medicinal use: astringent, carminative, diuretic, stimulant, vulnerary

It is one of the best cleansing herbs known and has even been credited with being able to break up kidney stones.

An infusion made by pouring 600 ml/l pint boiling water over 30 g/l oz dried plant and taken in wineglass doses several times a day will stimulate the action of the liver and kidneys, rid the body of accumulated poisons and water and ease inflammations of the stomach, the genito-urinary tract and the joints.

It is also a wound herb—the crushed leaves can be applied directly to a wound and will disinfect it, staunch bleeding and draw the tissues together.

It was a favourite tea herb for the Americans after the Boston Tea Party, the famous event when chests of tea were slung into the harbour in protest against the tax being levied on it. It was part of what they called "Liberty tea", a mixture of redclover flowers and leaves, wood betony and the leaves of the redroot bush and was very popular.

GOLDEN SEAL (Orange root)

Hydrastis canadensis

Family: Ranunculaceae
Parts used: root

This perennial is not one for the home gardener—it needs moisture and shade and five years growth before the root is ready for gathering. It is one of the finest medicinal plants in the herbal kingdom and fortunately the dried root can be obtained commercially.

Anyone who is prepared to persevere will have a low-growing plant with a hairy stem two dark green, deeply-cut, wrinkled leaves and one small greenish-white flower and a strange, bright yellow root with a liquoricey scent.

The root can be used as a dye.

Golden seal is best taken under the direction of a qualified herbalist or homoeopath.

It is used to treat allergies, asthma, bleeding, internal and external, burns, colds, colitis, constipation, diabetes, digestive upsets, eye infections, hay fever, infectious fevers, kidney, liver and spleen disorders, skin disorders, syphillis, tonsillitis, ulcers, vaginal discharge and voice loss. The list of conditions for which it can be used is the most impressive of all the medicinal herbs.

GROUND IVY (Creeping Jenny)

Glechoma hederacea

Family: Labiatae
Parts used: leaves

Ground ivy is a perennial evergreen with kidney-shaped, dark green leaves, scalloped round the edges and 2-lipped, bluish purple flowers which grow in the axils of the leaves at the top of the stem. It grows wild in many parts of the world and is a great ground-cover and an attractive plant but introduced into a garden it can run riot.

Medicinal use: astringent, diuretic, tonic

It is a good tonic. Tea made from the leaves is said to be good for anaemia, weak digestion, lazy kidneys and delayed menstruation.

A poultice made from the leaves with the addition of some yarrow and chamomile flowers will bring a stubborn boil or carbuncle to bursting point.

GROUNDSEL

Senecio vulgaris

Family: Compositae
Parts used: leaves and stems

Groundsel is a common weed which grows all over the world and stays in flower for many months. It is low-growing and quick-spreading with small leaves and tiny yellow flowers.

Medicinal use: diaphoretic, diuretic

A well-proven remedy for pain and stress of an irregular menstrual cycle is a decoction of 60 g/2 oz fresh groundsel to 1 litre/2 pints of water.

A weak groundsel tea will relieve biliousness and soothe chapped hands—a really strong one will act as a purgative.

HAWTHORN (May, Whitethorn)

Crataegus oxyacantha

Family: Rosaceae
Parts used: leaf-buds, flowers and berries

Hawthorn is a northern hemisphere deciduous shrub which can grow to the size of a small tree, though it is most often used as hedging. The pretty white flowers which cover the spiny bush in Spring are followed by small red berries. The small, glossy leaves, particularly when in bud, are a favourite nibble of country children who call them "bread and cheese".

Hawthorn seems able to grow anywhere and in any type of soil, in sun or in shade.

To grow a hawthorn hedge plant shrubs at 30 cm/12 inches apart and trim between midsummer and midspring.

It propagates easily from cuttings.

Culinary use: Country people have long used the flowers in milk and puddings and made jelly from the berries.

Medicinal use: antispasmodic, cardiac, diuretic, sedative, tonic

Hawthorn has been known for centuries as a heart herb. It has properties which make it a strong cardiac tonic and even a remedy for organic and functional disorders of the heart. It can regulate blood pressure, whether high or low, and since it is non-toxic, can be taken for a long period at a time, unlike other drugs which build up in the system with unpleasant results. It has been said that if an infusion is taken as soon as the first symptoms of angina appear there is a chance that the attack will not develop.

Tea made from the flowers is a good night-cap though its taste is rather bitter, so honey and lemon are needed to disguise it. Tea from the dried berries comforts loose bowels.

Caution: As a medicine hawthorn is best taken under professional advice.

HOPS

Humulus lupulus

Family: Cannabinaceae
Parts used: buds, young leaves, young tips and dried flower-cones

The plant is a perennial climber of great vigour, with squarish, thick stems, and pale-green, rough, toothed leaves like those of the vine. The flowers are greenish-white—some are female and are small and round when young, cone-shaped as they mature. The male flowers hang in loose clusters. There are male and female plants, and though only the female flowers are used in beer -making, male plants are often grown near-by because fertilised cones grow more rapidly and become larger than unfertilised ones.

Hops like a cool climate, full sun and a good organic soil.

Propagation can be made from cuttings or suckers.

A few female plants make a pleasant addition to the garden. The vines can climb as high as 10 m/33 ft. They make a clockwise ascent of any wires, pergola or trellis provided and can be used to smother unwanted shrubs or garden features. Plants should be cut down when the cones are ripe enough for drying.

The leaves cab be boiled to make a brown dye.

Culinary use: The young shoots can be cooked as for asparagus tips.

Medicinal use: anodyne, diuretic, sedative, tonic

Tea made from the dried cones aids the digestion, calms the nerves, relieves menstrual pains and cramps and helps insomniacs. It also soothes the male sexual responses, relieving the pain of constant erection and too frequent involuntary ejection of semen.

Hop poultices can be applied to boils and swellings.

Sprinkle flowers with alcohol and add to pillows to induce sleep.

HOREHOUND

Marrubium vulgare

Family: Labiateae
Parts used: leaves

The sprawling habit and less than handsome green and white wrinkled, hairy leaves and small white flowers of horehound do not make it the most welcome of garden plants but it is well worth having not only for its medicinal properties but also for its cheerful ability to thrive in spots where nothing else will. It will also bring bees into the garden.

It self-seeds well.

It should not be confused with the black horehound—*Ballota nigra*—which has the same sort of leaves but purple flowers and a terrible odour.

Medicinal use: expectorant, diuretic, laxative, tonic, vermifuge

Our horehound contains iron, potassium and the drug marrubin which stimulates the appetite, livens the liver, eases the coughing-up of stubborn phlegm and the expulsion of both the after-birth and worms. Pregnant women should not take it.

Tea made from the dried leaves is good for coughs, colds and flu.

Since it helps the body to get rid of excess water it can be considered a slimming herb—but the tea has to be made fairly strong and the taste is not too good and you have to be prepared for its laxative effect.

Horehound tea, horehound beer and horehound candy all give health and bring cheer.

HORSERADISH (Mountain radish)

Amoracia rusticana

Family: Cruciferae
Parts used: root

The plant is a tall perennial, with large, lance-shaped leaves, sometimes notched, and small white flowers. It needs a moist, organic soil in which the root can strike deep and plenty of sun.

Propagation is by root cuttings. Set the top of the sections about 2.5 cm/10 inches beneath the soil.

Medicinal use: diaphoretic, diuretic, stimulant

It has a high vitamin C content and can kill harmful bacteria in the intestinal tract—it stimulates the digestion and rids the body of excess water. Boiling water poured over some well-hammered root makes a tonic tea. Eating the root fresh or powdered will clear sinuses.

HORSETAIL (Pewterwort)
Equisetum arvense

Family: Equisitaceae
Parts used: stems

This is the last of a family of plants which flourished two hundred million years ago. It grows wild in temperate regions and, once in the garden, is there to stay. It likes moist soil and sun, but will tolerate shade.

Tough, hollow stems crowned with heads which look like miniature asparagus rise from a fast-creeping rhizome. The heads carry spores which are borne away by the wind and so effect propagation. The plant is virtually leafless, whorls of thin little branches, rather like the spokes of an umbrella, grow around the nodes along the stems.

Medicinal use: Astringent, antiseptic, diuretic, stomachic, tonic

The plant has a high silica content and is rich in vitamins and minerals but it is wiser to use it under professional guidance for it also contains selenium which can cause birth defects and equisitine which is a nerve poison. One way in which it can be safely used without supervision is as a treatment for head lice. A strong brew of the chopped stems used as a hairwash will kill both the nits and their eggs.

Horsetail has long been used for kidney or urinary problems and bleeding, both internal and external. The Chinese and the Gold Rush miners used it for rheumatoid arthritis and housewives have scoured their pots with it.
Not least of its capabilities is its ability to absorb gold dissolved in water.

HYSSOP
Hyssopus officinalis

Family: Labiatae
Parts used: whole plant

The Greek *hyssopos* may derive from the Hebrew *ezob*, meaning holy herb, because it was used to purify temples and the ritual cleaning of lepers: "Purge me with hyssop, and I shall be clean" (*Psalm 51 v.7*).

Hyssop is a pleasant, bushy, deciduous plant with neat, narrow leaves and blue to purple flowers (you may find white and pink varieties if you ask around). The plant gives off a scent somewhere between rosemary and camphor. Bees and butterflies love it. It likes a loose, well-drained soil and plenty of sun.

Propagation is by cuttings or root division.

Culinary use: A few chopped leaves added to a fatty dish will make it easier to digest but very little is needed as the flavour is decidedly pungent. The fresh flowers look pretty in salads, the dried ones in potpourri.

Medicinal use: anthelmintic, carminative, febrifuge, pectoral, stimulant

Hyssop is a good wound herb—the mould that produces penicillin grows on its leaf and its antiseptic properties make it widely useful. The tea makes an eyewash, a gargle, a "wormer", a liver livener and a soothing lotion for insect bites and stings, as well as a good garden spray when bacterial diseases are around.

JUNIPER
Juniperus communis

Family: Cupressus
Parts used: berries, leaves and wood

This slow-growing coniferous evergreen will grow to 3 m/10 ft in a sheltered spot or crouch low against a cold prevailing wind and make a stubby little bush. It will grow well in a garden in a temperate area.

There are male and female plants. The male flowers are yellow; the female blue-green and they grow in the leaf axils. The female flowers are followed by berries which ripen over a period of 3 years, turning from green to silver to blue-black.

Propagation is best made from semi-hardwood cuttings in early autumn. You need to have male and female plants growing together for the production of berries. The berries dry easily in the sun.

Culinary use: A leaf or two under grilling food or twigs burning on a barbecue will give food a juniper flavour. A few berries in stuffings, pate, game dishes, coleslaw will do the same.

The berries are used to flavour gin and other spirits.

Medicinal use: antiseptic, carminative, depurative, stimulant
Chewing juniper berries when epidemics are about will help to ward off infection. Good to take on holidays in the tropics.

Thrown on an open fire the berries are a great fumigant. The smoke drawn through the nostrils and deep into the lungs will help a heavy cold.

A tea made from the berries is good for the stomach, liver and bladder. A tea made from twigs and added to bath water will relieve the pain of sciatica, lumbago and rheumatism—a poultice made from them will do the same.

Caution: Juniper is not advised for pregnant women.

LADY'S BEDSTRAW (Our Lady's bedstraw)
Galium verum

Family: Rubiaceae
Parts used: whole plant

The scented golden-yellow flowers and neat, narrow, shiny leaves of this little creeping perennial made it popular as a strewing herb in the Middle Ages and legend has it that the Virgin chose it to line her infant's crib. The flowers smell like lime-blossom honey, the dried leaves like hay.

Medicinal use: alterative, diuretic, laxative

Tea made from the leaves will settle the nerves, loosen the bowels, help the body to get rid of excess water by promoting urine, ease sufferers from "gravel", and make a very nice face-wash.

LADY'S MANTLE (Dewcup)
Alchemilla vulgaris

Family: Rosaceae
Parts used: whole plant

Lady's mantle is a pretty little plant with tiny yellowish-green flowers; lobed leaves shaped like a lion's pad are daintily toothed and softly hairy and grow at the end of delicate slender stems. Dew is held in their shallow cup. The plant is perennial, likes a cool climate and rich, moist soil.

Propagation is by division. Leaves can be picked for use in salads or for drying as needed.

Medicinal use: astringent, styptic, tonic

It has been called "the woman's herb" as tea made from the plant helps conception, prevents miscarriage and regulates the menstrual cycle.

Applied externally it is a good wound salve, cleansing, cooling and drying, and so is also good for desperate cases of adolescent acne.

LAVENDER
Lavendula officinalis

Family: Labiatae
Parts used: flowers and leaves

There are several different varieties in cultivation, notably English, French, Spanish and Italian. All are bushes of varying size and make good hedges. The stems are strong, sometimes twisted, the leaves are narrow, grey-green, sometimes downy, and give off a scented oil when pressed. The flowers are usually spikes of tiny mauve florets which lift from the plant on long stalks, up to 90 cm/3 ft. There is a rare white variety. Bees love lavender.

Lavenders like a limey, well-drained soil and plenty of sunshine.

Propagation is usually from stem cuttings. Seed is tricky.

The leaves can be picked for use fresh or dried at any time. Flowers should be picked as they open.

Culinary use: The crystallised flowers make an edible cake and sweet decoration. Sugar, vinegar and oil can all be flavoured by the use of the flowers.

Medicinal use: antiseptic, carminative, sedative, vulnerary

Tea made from the flowers and leaves is a gentle sedative.

The essential oil (which can be bought) is antiseptic. It can kill the streptococcus, typhoid and diphtheria bacilli. Rubbed in the hair it will kill lice. Rubbed on the skin it keeps insects away, and on rheumaticky joints gives some relief from pain. It has wide use in aromatherapy. A weak lavender tea is said to make a good douche for sufferers from leucorrhea.

In the home: Lavender is an essential part of potpourri. Sachets of the flowers will scent drawers, linen cupboards, wardrobes and give protection against moths.

LEMONGRASS
Cymbopogon citratus

Family: Poaceae
Parts used: leaves

This is a tall perennial grass densely tufted, with long, thin, reed-like leaves with a strong lemon scent.

Don't try to grow it if your local temperature ever goes below 13° C/55° F. It needs a moist soil in full sun and if it ever gets too cold or too dry it will perish. It dies down in winter and reappears when the weather is warm enough to suit it the following year. Watering regularly is essential.

Propagation is by division.

The leaves, fresh or dried, make the most delightful herbal tea. It is worth growing for that alone. Tip any left in the pot into the bath water.

The leaves for chopping into salads and for drying can be cut at any time.

LIME (Linden)
Tilea

Family: Tiliaceae
Parts used: flowers, leaves and bark

The lime tree is not a usual type of herb but has so many domestic uses that it is a pleasure to have in the garden. It is deciduous, has small or large heart-shaped toothed leaves, according to variety, and clusters of scented, pale yellow flowers which hang from a bract. Bees love it. The lime tree will grow in any temperate part of the world.

Medicinal use: antispasmodic, diaphoretic, diuretic, nervine, stimulant, soothing, tonic

The flowers have a light scent, rather like that of the jonquil, and can be used, fresh or dried to make a refreshing tea which is a gentle sedative. When a migraine headache threatens, lime tea can be the first line of defence. The tea should be strong and taken a several times a day. It is also good to take when influenza or bronchitis have started to take hold or diarrhoea will not go away.

If you peel away the dark, shiny bark you will reach the sapwood which can be used to make a tea which is good for rheumatism and sciatica and will act as a diuretic.

LIQUORICE
Glycyrrhiza glabra

Family: Leguminosae
Parts used: root

This pretty, bushy, perennial plant has long, narrow, dark green leaves which fold as night falls, and pale mauve to cream pea-type flowers. It needs rich, soil, hot summers and warm winters. If you can't offer it these, don't bother—all you will get is a woody root, unpleasant in taste.

It can be propagated from a piece of root which carries a "bud".

Plants should be set out wide apart. It takes 3-4 years for the root to be ready for harvest. Peel the root before using.

Medicinal use: antispasmodic, demulcent, expectorant, laxative, pectoral

Liquorice contains a natural hormone which acts like cortisone—when blood sugar falls too low, doses of liquorice will restore it to normal, and yet diabetics whose blood sugar is too high can take it without ill effect. It is a gentle laxative, is good for coughs and colds and stomach cramps. Chewing a piece of dried root will ease the most terrible thirst.

LOBELIA (Pukeweed)
Lobelia inflata

Family: Campanulaceae
Parts used: herb

There are many members of the family and mistakes could be made. It is best to buy lobelia for use as a home medicine rather than using any garden plant.

L. inflata is an annual plant which grows about a metre high, has pale blue flowers and toothed, pointed hairy leaves. The stems give off a milky juice. When burned the plant smells like tobacco.

Medicinal use: anti-asthmatic, expectorant, emetic, diaphoretic, stimulant

Its most important property is the ability to loosen mucus on the chest and is especially useful for babies who don't know how to "hawk" to get rid of it.

Use the powdered herb or liquid extract, both obtainable commercially, for croup, asthma and whooping cough. Tea made from the powdered herb is good for the first stages of liver and stomach disorders.

LOVAGE (Smellage)
Levisticum officinale

Family: Umbelliferae
Parts used: leaves and seeds

Lovage is a tall, handsome, slow-growing perennial with glossy green leaves that smell like celery and umbels of pale yellow flowers. Bees love the plant. It needs warmth, rich moist light soil and part shade. Propagation is by division.

The leaves should be picked for drying before the flowers appear. The seeds should be brown before being harvested.

Culinary use: Lovage's sharpish, yeasty taste enlivens vegetable soups and vegetarian dishes—a snippet or so of leaf does the same for a salad. The chopped stems can be used as a vegetable or candied.

The seeds can be sprinkled over savoury scones.

Medicinal use: carminative, diuretic
The country name comes from the plant's ability to act as a deodorant. A strong lovage tea added to the bathwater or a few lovage leaves about the person will help.

The tea is also good for stomach wind and cystitis. The ground seed can be used like pepper or to make a warming drink.

Indians chew the stem believing it to be protection against cholera.

MAIDENHAIR FERN (Venus hair)
Adiantum capillus-veneris

Family: Filices
Parts used: leaves and stems

This well-known houseplant is less well-known as a medicinal herb.
It needs moisture, shade and an acid, well-drained soil. It does not like bought fertilisers.

Medicinal use: expectorant, pectoral
A tea made from the chopped leaves and stems is good for asthma and any troublesome cough and as a rinse for dull, lifeless hair.

MARIGOLD (POT)
Calendula officinalis

Family: Compositae
Parts used: flower petals and leaves

This hardy perennial, usually grown as an annual, adapts to any type of soil, likes a temperate climate and plenty of sun. It has sticky angular stems up to 60 cm/2 ft with long oval leaves, hairy and fleshy and larger at the base. The Romans called it "calendula" because it puts out some of its orange-gold flowers in every month of the year.

Popular old-fashioned cottage garden plants, pot marigolds are propagated from seed.

Culinary use: The bright petals have a piquant flavour and are used fresh in salads, and dried in soups, stews, home-made cheeses, rice puddings and cakes to give flavour and colour. If a recipe specifies saffron, try the much less expensive marigold petals instead.

Medicinal use: diaphoretic, stimulant The bruised leaves give off a strong, clean acrid scent. Applied to a stubborn corn, night and morning, the corn will soon come out. Some crushed flowers pressed against a bee or wasp sting will take away the pain.

Calendula, as it is called when used medicinally, is wonderful antiseptic for cuts and bruises and eases the pain of bruises and sprains almost as well as arnica. Tea made from the petals will reduce fevers and applied locally is good for painful varicose veins, burns or scalds. Tincture and ointment are found in most health food shops.

The petal tea was once used to turn the hair golden; used on material it produces a deep cream colour.

MARJORAM (Joy of the Mountains)
Origanum marjorana

Family: Labiatae
Parts used: stems and leaves

The cultivated marjoram comes from the wild plant oregano found on dry, fertile hillsides, usually on chalk and has a milder, sweeter taste. Oregano is strong, tangy and peppery.

Sweet marjoram makes a neat, bushy plant about 25 cm/10 inches in height, with small, soft, grey-green leaves and small white flowers which grow in clusters at the top of the stems. The whole plant has a clean, sweet scent. It attracts bees and butterflies.

It likes a fairly dry, chalky soil, plenty of sun and no frost. The seeds are very fine and transplanting can be very finicky so propagation is more easily done by taking cuttings.

In cool climates it should be treated as an annual, in warm ones as a biennial or perennial. After a few years plants need replacing because they get too woody. The stems, bearing leaves and flowers should be picked for drying just before the flowers are at their best. They dry quickly.

Culinary use: The chopped leaves give flavour to vegetables, salads, sauces, meat, poultry, fish and egg dishes, scones, omelettes etc. A tasty vinegar is made by filling a bottle with crushed leaves and then carefully dribbling in some wine or cider vinegar until the bottle will hold no more. Screw up lightly and leave in the sun for 2 weeks—then strain and rebottle. Oregano has a stronger flavour and can be bought dried.

Medicinal use: emmenogoguic, stimulant, tonic

Tea made from the leaves is both a tonic and a "soother". It helps morning sickness, travel sickness, uneasy digestion insomnia, vague aches and pains and disquiets.

Bruised leaves pressed around an aching tooth will ease the pain. Powdered ones pressed on a cold sore will help to heal it.

Marjoram contains a volatile oil which can be used as a rubbing oil. Cut up a handful of bruised leaves and put in a bottle, add a healthy dash or two of cider vinegar then fill up the bottle with sunflower seed oil. Screw up tightly and leave in the sun or a place that stays warm for about 3 weeks. Give the bottle a shake every time you visit it. Strain and rebottle.

Cosmetic use: Strong marjoram tea makes a good hair conditioner and a relaxing bath.

In the home: The dried flowers and leaves add scent to potpourri and made into small sachets make a fragrant aid to sleep and a sweet-smelling disinfectant for drawers and cupboards that have begun to smell stale.

Sweet marjoram was introduced to Europe in the Middle Ages and was in demand by ladies as "sweet bags" and "washing waters" and the leaves rubbed over heavy oak furniture.

Add pulverized leaves or a strong decoction to furniture polish.

MARSHMALLOW (Mortification root)
Althaea officinalis

Family: Malvaceae
Parts used: leaves and root

Marshmallow is a very tall perennial with a thick, hairy stem, toothed, hairy grey-green leaves and rose-pink 5-petalled flowers which grow in the leaf axils. It has a thick, yellow root.

This less spectacular relation of the hollyhock grows wild in marshes and bogs—introduced into the garden it makes a good back-of-the border plant. It needs regular watering and protection from the cold in winter.

To harvest, collect seeds when ripe, pick leaves as required and dig up roots in autumn. Propagation is by division or stem cuttings.

Culinary use: The peeled root used to be candied to make a sweetmeat. The marsh mallows of today are not the same thing.

The flowers and young leaves can be used in salads. The root, boiled then fried makes a different vegetable.

Medicinal use: demulcent, emollient A tea (30 g/1oz leaves to 600 ml/1 pint boiling water) taken frequently in wineglassful doses is said to be good for cystitis and colitis. It can also be used to bathe sore eyes.

The chopped root mixed with water produces a gel which is good for chafed skin, sunburn, burns, wounds. It was called "mortification root" because the old country people found it prevented gangrene setting in.

Cosmetic use: Boil leaves or use the liquid from steeped root, warmed or cold, as a soothing mucilage for dry hands, sunburn and dry hair and in facial steams, masks and lotions. it can be used to make a shampoo for dry hair.

Marshmallow ointment and shampoo can be bought at most health food shops.

MEADOWSWEET (Queen of the meadow)
Filipendula ulmaria

Family: Rosaceae
Partsused: whole plant

One of the loveliest of European wild plants, meadowsweet lifts its tall stems in summer in ditches, water meadows, the banks of streams. It loves moisture. The pale froth of tiny blossoms carry a honeyed, almond fragrance; the dark green serrated leaves, which are silvery and downy on the underside, are less heady. When dried they have the clean scent of new-mown hay. Introduced into a garden in temperate regions, meadowsweet will settle quite happily in sun or part-shade as long as the soil is moist and rich. Plants can be divided in the autumn.

Pick leaves for drying before the flowers appear and pick flowers when young and fresh. Both are useful in potpourri. A yellowish dye can be made from the flowers, a blue one from the leaves and stems and a black one from the roots.

Culinary use: The plant is rich in vitamin C and makes a good summertime drink. Gives a slight almond flavour to jams and stewed fruit.

Medicinal use: astringent, diuretic
The flowers contain salicylic acid, a constituent of aspirin, so a tea made from them can be used as a mild sedative and pain reliever. A tea made from the flowers and leaves will bring on perspiration and "break" a feverish cold, help rid the body of excess fluid and alleviate heartburn. Not only that, it will settle an upset stomach and, because of its astringent quality, reduce diarrhoea. A decoction made by boiling the root is a good wound salve.

Cosmetic use: Soak flowers in water in the sun all day, strain and use the liquid as a tonic for an open oily skin.

MELILOT (Hart's clover)
Melilotus officinalis

Family: Leguminoseae
Parts used: flowers and leaves

Melilot is a tall biennial which grows wild in temperate regions and has been much used as a fodder crop. It grows to about 1 metre/3 feet in height, has branched stems of dark leaves which grow in threes and small yellow pea-type flowers which grow in the leaf axils. Leaves and flowers have a sweet scent. Bees love the plant. Introduced into the garden it will self-seed happily.

Culinary use: It is good in stuffing (particularly for rabbit), marinades and herb beers.

Medicinal use: antiseptic, antispasmodic, carminative, diuretic, emollient, sedative

Strong tea made from the leaves and flowers taken regularly will strengthen the walls of the veins and bring relief to sufferers from varicose veins. A milder tea made just from the flowers helps flatulence, retention of urine, painful menstruation and insomnia. A milder one still makes a good bath for sore eyes.

In the home: Dried melilot leaves in the wardrobe keep moths and stale smells away. Dried leaves and flowers add to the fragrance of potpourri.

MINT
Mentha spp.

Family: Labiatae
Parts used: leaves

There are many different varieties of mint and if more than one is grown it is wise to keep them well apart or they will cross-breed and lose their individuality. Flowerheads should be picked on sight.

Mints are creeping plants with square stems, aromatic leaves and whorls of purplish-white or pinkish flowers, according to variety. They need a fairly rich soil, some shade and plenty of water. The common mint *(mentha arvenis)* can take more sun than can *M. spicata* (spearmint) or *M. suavolens* (apple mint). All mints are intrusive. Propagation is by division.

Culinary use: *M. spicata* (spearmint) with its deep green, hairless leaves is the best one to use. Yoghurt and chopped mint leaves make a good salad dressing. Try some mashed dates with a touch of lemon juice and some chopped mint as a sandwich filling.

Add to soft cheeses, marmalades, chutneys, cooked vegetables, and of course, use as mint sauce with lamb.

Orange bergamot mint has reddish stems, dark-green leaves with red edges and purple flowers. The leaves have a strong, lemon taste good for salads.

Medicinal use: Peppermint *(M. peperita)* has an oil which contains menthol. A few bruised leaves applied to an insect sting will relieve the pain.

Mint tea is good for indigestion and vomiting.

Cosmetic use: Eau-de-cologne mint smells just like eau-de-cologne and gives fragrance to the bath or washing water. A muslin bag containing the leaves can be dropped in the water or a mint tea can be poured in.

In the home: Bruised mint leaves around the floors will keep mice away.

MOTHERWORT (Herb of life)
Leonur cardiaca

Family: Labiatae
Parts used: whole herb

Motherwort belongs to the nettle family and grows wild in temperate areas. It has square stems, dark-green, serrated, hairy leaves with prominent veins on the underside and pink flowers growing in whorls in the leaf-axils at the top of the stem.

Medicinal use: antispasmodic, emmenogoguic, nervine, tonic

This is a good herb to know about, if not to grow. It is one of the most respected female tonics, acting on the generative organs and the heart gently and effectively. It is good for the irritability of overstrain, the "shakes" and bodily weakness which results in suppression of the menses. It can be found in powdered or in liquid form at most good herbalists.

In the home: The whole plant is used to make a dark green dye.

MUGWORT (St. John's plant)
Artemesia vulgaris

Family: Compositae
Parts used: roots and leaves

There are several species of the common mugwort—all are tall, attractive, sweetly scented plants with purple stems, dark green or grey feathery leaves and tiny yellow flowers. Grown as border plants they bring bees into the garden. They all like well-drained soil and full sun. The roots are invasive.

Propagation is by cuttings or root division. The leaves and tips should be gathered for drying just before the flowers come out.

The root, which should be dried whole, is dug up at the end of the flowering season.

Culinary use: A few mugwort leaves make a substitute for tarragon. A few with goose and pork dishes will make the fat easier to digest.

Medicinal use: diaphoretic, diuretic, emmenogoguic, vermifuge

Mugwort is best known for its ability to promote the menstrual flow and as a sovereign remedy for the menopause. Tea from the leaves taken for a few days each month is said to be effective in both cases. It will also act as a tonic when appetite fails. The powdered leaves, taken in wine, ease the pain of sciatica.

The dried root, made into an infusion and taken in small doses will expel worms without being drastic about it.

In the home: Muslin bags of mugwort leaves among woollies will keep moths away. The dried flowers add colour to potpourri.

MULLEIN (Beggars' blanket, Our Lady's flannel, Bullocks' lungwort)
Verbascum thapsus

Family: Scrophulariaceae
Parts used: flowers and leaves

Mullein grows wild in temperate zones, flourishing in wastelands exposed to the sun and with little water. It is a biennial.

The flowering stem rises about 2 m/6 feet from a rosette of huge, woolly, grey-green pointed leaves at ground level and bears a handsome spike of yellow flowers. Stems and leaves are covered with a fine, pale down.

The root bores deep into the earth. It makes a handsome garden plant very attractive to bees.

Mullein can be grown from seed but will have to be watched as it does not like a lot of moisture but nevertheless needs some to stay alive. The plants need space and will not flower the first year. Once established they self-sow all too readily.

Pick leaves and flowers for drying in the summer.

Medicinal use: astringent, demulcent, expectorant, sedative (mild)

Tea made from leaves and flowers is good for loosening a stubborn cough, hence the country name Bullock's lungwort. Honey is the best sweetener to use with it.

The plant contains mucilage which swells and become slippery as it takes in water so it is able to soothe sore throats and chests. It is also good for insomniacs and sufferers from hay-fever and diarrhoea. A strong tea, cooled and made into a compress, will ease the pain of piles.

A poultice made from bruised boiled leaves is good for skin irritations and inflammations.

Note: The tea should be well-strained to get rid of any hairs which might cause irritation.

Poultices should be wrapped in cloth before being applied.

Cosmetic use: A strong tea made from the yellow flowers will brighten fair hair which is fading.

MUSTARD
Brassica nigra

Family: Cruciferae
Parts used: flowers and leaves, seeds

Black mustard is an annual which can grow to 2 m/6 ft in height and has bristly spiked leaves and bright yellow flowers with the calyx and corolla growing in a cruciform pattern. The leaves are small, oval, pointed, dark-green on the surface and paler underneath and have a pungent flavour.

Mustard likes a rich soil and light shade. Sow in Spring. The seed-pods should be collected before they open and spill the seed. Mustard is a good companion plant for cabbage—it keeps the cabbage white butterfly at bay.

Culinary use: The young leaves and flowers can be added to salads. The seeds are used in meat casseroles and pickles and to make mustard sauce.

Medicinal use: diuretic, emetic, irritant, stimulant

If it is necessary to induce vomiting, stir some dried mustard powder into a cup of warm water and drink at once.

If chilled to the bone, add mustard powder to the bath water. The volatile oil it contains will bring the blood to the surface of the skin and get the circulation going.

MYRTLE

Myrtus communis

Family: Myrtaceae
Parts used: flowers, leaves, berries

This tall evergreen shrub has glossy dark-green aromatic leaves and creamy-white, many-stamened flowers which are followed by shiny black berries. It makes a handsome garden plant. Myrtle needs good soil, sun and protection from frost.

Propagation is easy—summer cuttings or layering are equally successful.

Culinary use: The dried leaves and berries can be used in stuffings for hare and venison.

A branch on the barbecue will give pork and lamb a spicy flavour.

Medicinal use: pulmonary
Tea made from the leaves has an astringent and antiseptic effect and will help chest complaints, vaginal discharge, psoriasis, sinusitis. Made into a compress it will reduce the pain and pressure of piles.

In the home: Add dried leaves and flowers to potpourri.

A decoction of the berries, used as a rinse, makes dark hair glossy.

NASTURTIUM

Tropaeolum majus

Family: Tropaeolaceae
Parts used: leaves, flowers and seeds

Nasturtiums are annual creeping and climbing plants with clean green, flat, round or kidney-shaped juicy leaves and helmet-shaped flowers of colours ranging from sharp yellow, through orange to bright scarlet. They don't mind a poor soil—a rich one will encourage stems and leaves but not flowers—but they must have sun. They self-seed.

Culinary use: The leaves (which are rich in vitamin C) have a tangy, peppery taste and, with the flowers, liven a plain salad and sandwich fillings. The pickled seeds can be used instead of caper sauce.

Medicinal use: antibiotic, diuretic, purgative

Anyone allergic to penicillin should try nasturtiums—they are rich in sulphur and are a natural antibiotic which does not destroy the intestinal flora.

Drinking fresh tea made from a handful of chopped leaves and boiling water three times a day, and using the crushed fruits to make a poultice will draw boils and abscesses and clear the infection. The tea makes a good face wash for acne suffers.

Cosmetic use: Equal quantities of nasturtium flowers and leaves and nettle leaves, well-chopped and left to soak in alcohol (bought at the chemist) for a fortnight will, when strained, make a scalp-rub when the hair is dull and comes out too easily.

In the garden: Nasturtiums are good companion plants. Insects do not like their mustardy scent. Aphids do not like nasturtiums.

NETTLE

Urtica dioica

Family: Urticaceae
Parts used: leaves, flowers, seeds, roots

There are many different varieties of nettle. *U. dioica* is the familiar stinging nettle. It has tall, square stems, dark green pointed serrated leaves and both male and female flowers. The male ones are green and erect, the female are longer and droop.
Leaves and stems sting when touched.

Nettles will grow almost anywhere and are among the most valuable plants known to man. They can be propagated by root division after the leaves have died back. Leaves are gathered for drying before the flowers come out.

Culinary use: Nettles contain chlorophyll, protein, iron, silica, sulphur, potassium, sodium and vitamins A, B and C. The fresh, young tops do not sting and can be used in salads; the leaves, soaked to draw out the sting, make a good cooked vegetable. Nettle beer used to be a favourite country drink. Chopped nettles added to chicken, pig and horse food make a good animal tonic.

Medicinal use: anti-diabetic, anti-anaemic, astringent, diuretic, depurative, emmenogoguic, haemostatic, irritant, stimulant, vermifuge

Cosmetic use: Tea made from the boiled roots rubbed into the scalp every day will cure dandruff and falling hair.

In the garden: Nettle tea made from the leaves makes a good spray against aphids. The plant, chopped and soaked in water, makes a fine liquid manure.

OREGANO (See Marjoram)

PARSLEY

Petroselinium crispum

Family: Umbelliferae
Parts used: leaves, stems and roots

The plant is biennial with dark, green feathery leaves, either plain or curly, juicy stems and a long taproot. It needs a rich soil with plenty of humus, regular watering and not too much sun.

The flowers, which are not wanted and take strength from the leaves, appear in the second year so most gardeners prefer to treat parsley as an annual. The seed takes about 6 weeks to germinate. Soaking in water before planting will speed things up.

Culinary use: Parsley contains vitamins A, B and C. The roots have more vitamin C than oranges. The Hamburg variety has the largest roots. The leaves are used as a garnish, whole, chopped or even fried and are added, together with the stems which are full of flavour and nutriment, to casseroles, stews, sauces and stuffings, butter and cream and cottage cheese. And what is fish without parsley sauce? Or life without tabouleh, the healthy Middle-Eastern dish?

Medicinal use: antiseptic, diuretic, emmenogoguic, expectorant, stomachic. Parsley tea is good for upset stomachs, kidney and bladder trouble, menstrual cramps and rheumatism.

Chewed leaves sweeten the breath.

Bruised leaves and stems ease the pain of wounds and insect bites.

Cosmetic use: Soaking leaves in hot water and applying them to the face when cool will help acne. The water can also be used as a facewash or shampoo.

In the garden: A border of parsley will protect other plants against aphids and improve the taste of fruit and vegetables and the scent of rose. Bees love it.

PARSLEY PIERT (Breakstone)

Alchemilla arvensis

Family: Rosaceae
Parts used: leaves

This tiny annual has small, downy, deeply lobed pale green leaves and tiny yellow flowers which grow in clusters. It grows wild on stony barren ground in temperate parts of the world. Young plants can be introduced into the garden where they will settle in and self-seed each year.

Culinary use: The leaves have a pleasant taste in salads.

Medicinal use: Demulcent, diuretic
The country name "Breakstone" indicates its use as a remedy for gravel in the bladder, retention of urine and all kidney complaints. Tea made from the leaves should be taken 3 times a day in cupful doses.

PASSION FLOWER

Passiflora incarnata

Family: Passifloraceae
Parts used: leaves

The ornamental blue passionflower *P. caerulea* contains poison. *P. incarnata* has a perennial root and puts out fast-growing climbing stems each year. The leaves are serrated, lobed and dull green, the flowers are white, tinged with purple and sweetly scented. The fruits are yellowish and egg-shaped.

Passionflowers need a rich, well-drained soil, plenty of water and light, a trellis or other structure over which to climb and protection against hot sun.

Propagation is from root runners, stem cuttings or seed. Leaves should be picked for drying when flowers are in full bloom.

Culinary use: The fruits can be eaten.

Medicinal use: Bruised leaves pressed against a wound make a good first-aid treatment.

Passionflower calms the nervous system promotes sleep. One teaspoonful dried leaves infused in a cup of boiling water and left to grow cool makes a good, relaxing night-cap.

Passiflora relaxes the muscles and so can ease the digestive tract and the reproductive organs. It is said to be good for the heart too. A herbalist will advise on this.

Caution: avoid during pregnancy.

PENNYROYAL (Pudding grass, Flea mint)

Mentha pulegium

Family: Mint species
Parts used: leaves and flowers

The European pennyroyal is a low-growing creeping perennial plant with small, oval, hairy leaves and tiny lilac flowers. It likes a moist soil and a shady spot. Propagation is by division or stem cuttings. The American variety is an annual, grows upright to about 25 cm/ 9 inches, has pointed leaves and pale blue flowers, and likes a sandy soil in full sun. Because of its strong scent, Pennyroyal is popular as an aromatic ground-cover, a garden edging and in the joints of paving stones.

The leaves and flowers should be harvested when the plant is in full bloom. It is propagated from seeds.

Culinary use: The leaves can be used instead of mint but the taste is much stronger.

Medicinal use: carminative, diaphoretic emmenogoguic, sedative, sudorific
The strong peppermint flavour of pennyroyal tea is warming and comforting when chill has struck, the stomach is upset, nerves are jangled, the chest is tight, menstruation is delayed or children are suffering from whooping cough (but not if they are under two).

It is unsuitable for pregnant women as it has an effect on the uterus. Anyone thinking of taking the oil to terminate an unwanted pregnancy should think again—even a small amount can be lethal.

In the home: Leaves rubbed on the skin to release the plant's oil will act as an insect repellent. Rubbed into a pet's fur and on to sleeping blankets they will keep fleas away. Leaves scattered in food cupboards will keep ants away.

The dried flowers and leaves are excellent for potpourri.

PERIWINKLE (Joy of the ground)
Vinca major and V. minor

Family: Apocynaceae
Parts used: leaves

Both varieties are evergreen with glossy, oval leaves and open-faced, blue flowers. Periwinkles are creeping plants which can be invasive but make an excellent ground-cover in almost any type of soil and in sun or shade. Propagation is by division or stem cuttings.

Medicinal use: astringent, tonic, vulnerary

A weak tea made from the leaves is astringent and will dry internal or external haemorrhage and ease diarrhoea. It is a relation of *V. rosea*, a South African plant said to be more effective than insulin in the treatment of diabetes. A herbalist will advise on dosage.

PLANTAIN (Rat's tail)
Plantago major

Family: Plantaginaceae
Parts used: leaves

This is the largest member of a large family. It grows about half a metre high, has an erect stalk and large oval, veined leaves growing in a rosette at the base of the plant and spikes of tiny yellow-green or pinkish flowers. It likes a well-drained soil and full sun. Propagation is from seed.

Culinary use: The young leaves can be eaten like spinach.

Medicinal use: Alterative, astringent, de-obstruent, diuretic emmenogoguic, styptic, vulnerary

A weak tea made from the leaves will rid the body of excess water if drunk regularly. A stronger one will help with fevers, asthma, worms and sinusitis. When cool it can be used as a gentle enema to relieve the pain of piles.

A poultice of bruised leaves when hot will draw boils and carbuncles; when cool will relieve inflamed piles, burns and scalds.

Bruised leaves pressed on a wound will stop bleeding; on a nettle sting will be as effective as dock; on any insect bite will take away itching.

POPPY
Papaver

Family: Papaveraceae
Parts used: seeds

This family has to be understood.

There is *P. rhoeas*, the wild field poppy with a long slender stem, serrated leaves and a single red flower. *P. orientalis* a showy garden perennial which can grow a metre high and has large flowerheads, single or double in a wonderful colour range from white to pink, purple or red. This handsome plant needs a well-drained, good soil and very gentle sun.

And then there is *P. somniferum*, the opium poppy.

It is a tall, annual plant with coarse, serrated leaves and whitish-blue flowers with a purple mark at the base, and roundish, whitish seed-pods packed with grey seeds. It likes warmth but will grow in more temperate parts of the world, given plenty of sunshine and moisture. This is the poppy from which morphine and heroin is manufactured. No gardener should attempt to use it. If you grow it, no attempt should be made to use it. Its properties are such that the strictest professional supervision is needed for it to be used safely. Poppy seeds can be safely bought from food stores.

Culinary use: The crushed seeds are sprinkled over curry dishes, breads and pastries.

Medicinal use: Tea made from the seeds soothes jangled nerves, is gently soporific and eases the pain of toothache and ear-ache.

RASPBERRY
Rubus idaeus

Family: Rosaceae
Parts used: fruit and leaves

The one thing wrong with raspberries— just about everybody's favourite fruit—is that they will only grow where there are cool summers. The plant has perennial roots which throw up a mass of thorny stems bearing pointed, serrated leaves and small white flowers which are followed by succulent berries

Raspberries need a rich soil, some shade and a support on which the canes can grow. They fruit in the second year of growth, the fruiting canes then die and have to be cut out as new ones come up to take their place.

Propagation is made from root cuttings. The leaves can be harvested for drying at any time.

Culinary use: Rich in iron, vitamins A and the B elements, the fruit makes an excellent food or drink. It freezes well, retaining most of its properties.

Medicinal use: astringent, stimulant, sudorific, tonic

Raspberry vinegar taken in hot water is good for chills, vomiting and as gargle for a sore throat.

Raspberry leaf tea is a well-known tonic for the female reproductive organs—it eases painful menstruation and diarrhoea. It also makes a mildly astringent face-wash.

RED CLOVER
Trifolium pratense

Family: Leguminosae
Parts used: leaves and flowers

Clover is a perennial plant which grows wild in temperate regions. The dark-green leaves grow in groups of three at the end of a slender stem—a four-leafed clover is thought to be lucky. The flowers are pink-purple and grow in a fragrant ball. Country children suck the sweetness from them. Clover likes a good moist soil, not a sandy one, and plenty of sun.

Medicinal use: alterative, depurative, sedative

Clover tea, taken regularly, will steady the nerves, purify the blood and ease digestion. It can rid the body of toxins left after lengthy treatment with drugs and is a long-used remedy for whooping cough.

Externally it is used as a wash in cases of eczema and psoriasis.

ROSEMARY (Dew of the Sea)
Rosmarinus officinalis

Family: Laciatae
Parts used: leaves, flowers

Rosemary is a shrubby aromatic plant with thin dark-green leaves, silver on the underside and very strongly scented, small mauve-blue flowers which grow along the stems and at their tips. It makes good hedging. There is also a prostrate type which makes an excellent ground-cover.

Rosemary likes a light, well-drained soil and a place in the sun. Propagation can be made from heel cuttings, root division or layering.

Culinary use: The leaves, fresh or dried are good with meat dishes, particularly lamb. Rich dishes like roast duck and pork benefit from a touch of rosemary. A pinch of the dried herb will add flavour to soups, stews and sauces—a small sprig of the fresh herb in the milk for making puddings or custard makes a nice change. The flowers can be frosted by dipping them into beaten white of egg and sugar. When dry they make an edible garnish for cakes or salads.

Medicinal use: astringent, antispasmodic, antiseptic, carminative, diuretic, emmenogoguic, nervine, stimulant, tonic

A tea made from the flowering tips is good for headaches, strained nerves and retention of urine. In stronger concentration it will aid the expulsion of worms but should be used with care, and never by pregnant women.

Rosemary oil makes a good rub for painful rheumaticky joints as it stimulates the circulation.

Tea made from the leaves can be used as an antiseptic and gargle. Inhaling the steam from rosemary leaves covered by boiling water will help to clear blocked sinuses and relieve a cold.

Cosmetic use: Rosemary tea is a good hair-rise and face wash. Simmer the leaves for half an hour for a stronger hair tonic which is good for dandruff.

In the home: Moths and mosquitoes do not like the scent of rosemary.

In the garden: The taste of sage is improved if rosemary is grown nearby. Cabbage butterflies will keep away from cabbage growing near rosemary.

RUE (Herb of repentance)
Ruta graveolens

Family: Rutaceae.
Parts used: whole plant

Rue is a dainty evergreen plant which grows quite tall and has feathery blue-green leaves and pretty yellow flowers.

A variety which has metallic bluish leaves and is lower-growing makes a nice low hedging border plant. Rue likes full sun and a poor soil.

Culinary use: The leaf is used in salads and sandwiches.

Medicinal use: anthelmintic, antispasmodic, emmenogoguic, stimulant
Tea made from the flowers makes an eyebath said to prevent the formation of cataracts. Tea made from the leaves stimulates the bile, the appetite, perspiration and the menstrual flow. Since the plant contains iron and mineral salts the tea makes a good tonic which, though tasting bitter, is not unpleasant.

The plant contains rutin, one of the best substances for strengthening the blood vessels. Rutin is sold commercially as a remedy for high blood pressure. so drinking rue tea regularly makes good sense for sufferers from the condition.

Rue should be treated with care. An overdose could cause abortion.

SAGE
Salvia officinalis

Family: Labiateae
Parts used: leaves

Sage is a perennial rather bushy plant with grey-green leaves, smooth on the surface and rough underneath. The flowers are blue. Some varieties have red, white or pink ones.

It likes a well-drained soil and plenty of sun. Propagation is by cuttings or layering. Leaves should be picked for drying before the flowers come out.

Dry sage leaves very slowly. If they turn brown they will taste musty.

Culinary use: The leaves, used fresh or dried, have a strong, clean flavour which cuts the grease of fatty food so they are often used in stuffing for pork and goose, and with sausages. They are good in soups, stews, casseroles, home-made cheese. Chopped sage mixed with grated cheese makes a tasty sandwich filling.

Medicinal use: anti-inflammatory, digestive, nervine, oestrogenic, tonic

Sage tea is good for the nerves, depression and for drying up the milk of nursing mothers. It contains oestrogen and is used as a toner for the female reproductive organs. It can also clear mucus from the respiratory and digestive tracts, ease diarrhoea, and soothe coughs and colds.

A decoction of leaves, 15 g/½ oz to

a litre of water, boiled up and left to cool makes a gargle for sore throats, a mouthwash for inflamed gums, mouth ulcers and abscessed teeth. A leaf rubbed against the teeth each day will help to keep them white. A poultice of boiled leaves will help to ease painful wounds and suppurating boils. If body odour is a problem, chewing a few sage leaves each day could fix it.

Cosmetic use: Sage tea makes a good hair tonic that keeps the colour in dark hair.

In the home: Moths don't like the smell of sage.

In the garden: Dried sage between plants will protect them from mildew, the carrot-fly and the cabbage-moth.

ST. JOHN'S WORT

Hypericum perforatum

Family: Hypericaceae
Parts used: whole plant

This is a small perennial with reddish stems up to 90 cm/3 ft, small, pale green oval leaves which look dark because of the oil glands which dot them. Bright yellow flowers with long dark stamens appear in late summer. The flowers give out a dark-red oil when squeezed. The plant grows wild in Europe and Asia.

Medicinal use: astringent, diuretic, expectorant, sedative
Tea made from the dried leaves and flowers is good for coughs and colds, lung complaints, painful micturition, a torpid liver and agitation. The fresh flowers left to soak in olive oil for a month will give up their oil which can then be used as a wound and burn dressing and as a massage oil for painful joints and sprains.

Caution: Avoid exposure to sun during treatment. Plant causes photosensitivity.

SALAD BURNET

Poterium sanguisora

Family: Rosaceae
Parts used: leaves

Salad burnet is a pretty, low-growing perennial which makes a nice border plant for the main garden. It has lacey bright-green leaves and tiny reddish flowers. It likes lime in the soil and will grow in either sun or shade.

Leaves should be cut when young for use fresh. They do not dry too well.

Culinary use: The leaves have a sharp cucumber taste. Chopped they make a tasty addition to salads, cream and cottage cheese, fruit drinks and herb butter. The flavour is lost if the herb is cooked.

Medicinal use: carminative, tonic
Tea made from the leaves is fresh-tasting and acts as a stomach settler and tonic. Used externally it will also ease the pain of sunburn.

SANTOLINA (Cotton lavender)

Santolina chamaecyparissus

Family: Compositae
Parts used: leaves

Santolina is a low-growing little bushy plant with silver-grey, finely divided leaves which grow thickly along the lower stems above which yellow button-shaped flowers rise on clean tall stalks. The plant likes a sandy, well-drained soil, not a rich, one and plenty of sun. It can be clipped and made into an edging for the border, but it has to be done gently, the plant hates to be pruned hard. Propagation is by cuttings.

The flowers and leaves can be picked at any time for use fresh or for drying

Medicinal use: A mild tea made from the flowers and leaves will cleanse the kidneys and liver. A decoction is used for scabs and ringworm.

In the home: Dried flowers and leaves are decorative and can be added to pot-pourri. A few sprigs of santolina around the house—under carpets, in wardrobes or on book shelves will keep insects away.

SAVORY (Bean herb)

Satureja hortensis (Summer savory)
S. montana (Winter savory)
S. repandra (Low-growing Winter savory)

Low-growing winter savory makes a good ground cover but does not have the culinary and medicinal uses of the other two.

Summer savory is an annual plant with narrow, tender, brownish-green leaves and pale pink or lavender flowers. The stems are weak and the plant is untidy. It grows easily from seed.

Winter savory is a perennial with small leaves which are very pale when young but darken heavily with age. The flowers are tiny, pink to white.

All savories like full sun and a well drained soil. Pick leaves as flower buds are forming. Pick flower tops for drying at the beginning of autumn.

Culinary use: As a culinary herb it dates back to the early Romans; potent flavouring enhances all others in the same way as salt.

The leaves are sweetly spicy and peppery—winter savory has the sharper flavour. Used chopped in any bean dish they bring out the flavour. The leaves dry well and can be kept, wrapped in foil, in the freezer. People not allowed to use salt and pepper on medical grounds will enjoy a sprinkling of powdered savory over any savoury dish. Any food hard to digest will be less troublesome if served with a touch of savory.

Medicinal use: carminative, expectorant
Tea from the leaves will help a rattly cough. Leaves, pressed against a wasp or bee sting, will release volatile oil which will take the pain away.

SKULLCAP (Mad weed)
Scutellaria lateriflora

Family: Labiatae

The plant looks like its relation, the nettle,and has oval, serrated leaves and blue flowers. It grows wild in temperate parts of the world. It is such a useful medicinal plant that it is often found in gardens.

It likes well-drained, not rich soil in sun or shade. It can be propagated by division of the perennial root.

Medicinal use: antispasmodic, nervine, tonic

The herb can be bought powdered or in liquid extract. It is very effective against the terrible convulsions brought on by hydrophobia and is a specific for St. Vitus' Dance. Tea made from the powdered herb is good for rheumatism, neuralgia, mild hysteria and premenstrual tension.

SHEPHERD'S PURSE (Mother's heart)
Capsella bursa-pastoris

Family: Cruciferae
Parts used: whole plant

This little annual weed will grow almost anywhere. It ripens about half a million seeds in a season, so is found everywhere. It is an insignificant little plant with tiny narrow leaves and a cluster of white flowers at the end of a thin stem. These turn into heart-shaped or triangular seedpods.

Medicinal use: diuretic, stimulant, styptic

The plant has the active constituents choline, aminophenol, diosmin, acetychlorine and tyramine. Tea made from the dried plant, taken in wineglassful doses, will stop internal bleeding, control diarrhoea, ease cystitis and act on bladder and kidney stones.

Shepherd's purse is prescribed in homeopathic doses for excessive menses and menstrual pain. It is a womb tonic. Home dried shepherd's purse is best discarded after a year.

SOAPWORT (Bouncing Bet)
Saponaria officinalis

Family: Carophyllaceae
Parts used: leaves, stems and roots

Soapwort is a pretty, but poisonous plant with a weak stem that can grow up to a metre in height, smooth, pale green pointed leaves and pale pink flowers, single in the wild and double in cultivation. The flowers have a long, thin calyx and little scent in the leaves, stems and roots. Some find the scent delicious—a raspberry-clove verging on the bitter. The plant likes rich, moist soil and a little shade. It can be propagated by seed or root division.

It has no culinary use and should not be taken internally in home preparations or for medical conditions.

A decoction of the root can be used as a wash for sufferers from acne and psoriasis.

In the home: Cover the plant in rain water or purified tap water and boil for half an hour. The soapy liquid produced makes a splendid shampoo for hair, wool and all delicate fabrics.

SORREL
Rumex scutatus

Family: Polygonaceae
Parts used: leaves and flowers

This is the cultivated French sorrel—not the one that grows wild. The plant looks like the wild one—tall-stemmed slightly branching to 1.2 m/4 ft with spikes of reddish green flowers—but the leaves are smaller and broader (buckler-leafed sorrel), have a sharp lemony flavour, and are less acidic than their relations.

French sorrel likes good soil and a dry, sunny spot. Propagate from seed and by root division.

The leaves should not be used dried. Use fresh or keep them wrapped in foil, in the freezer until needed.

Culinary use: The leaves are used in soups, mayonnaise and salads. Young leaves, chopped and cooked in butter, add flavour to a white sauce or plain omelette.

Medicinal use: Tea made from the young leaves is a sharp-tasting, cooling drink which will cleanse the system and provide some vitamin C.

Caution: People suffering from asthma, rheumatism or renal colic should not use sorrel.

In the home: A strong tea (the plant contains oxalic acid) will remove verdigris on metals—the juice of the fresh leaves will loosen ink stains which can then be washed out.

SOUTHERNWOOD (Lad's love)
Artemisia abrotanum

Family: Compositae
Partsused: leaves

Southernwood is a smallish perennial shrub with a wealth of feathery, grey-green, aromatic leaves, the sweetest ones in the family, and tiny daisy-like flowers. The plant will straggle if it is not kept trimmed but trimmed it can make a neat hedge.

Propagation is best from cuttings or root division—seed take too long.

Medicinal use: antiseptic, astringent, emmenogoguic, nervine, stimulant, tonic

Southernwood tea, whether made from fresh or dried leaves, is bitter and needs honey to make it palatable.It has a pronounced effect on the female reproductive organs, toning them up and promoting the menstrual flow. It also acts as a general tonic and revitaliser. The powdered leaves mixed with honey or treacle and taken a teaspoonful at a time will help to expel threadworms.

In the home: Moths and ants do not like the smell of southernwood. Sachets in wardrobes, drawers and under carpets will keep them away.

In the garden: Grow near stone-fruit trees to help repel the fruit-fly and near garden ponds to repel the mosquito.

SWEET CICELY (Shepherd's needle)
Myrrhis odorata

Family: Umbelliferae

This tall perennial can be confused with cow-parsley. The stems are hollow, furrowed and hairy, the light-green feathery leaves are slightly hairy on the underside. The tiny white umbelliferous flowers, which bees love, produce seedheads which turn brown as they ripen and take root quickly wherever they fall. This can be circumvented by eating the seeds when they are green—they have a nice nutty taste. The plant likes a soil rich in humus, in sun or light shade.

Culinary use: The sugar content of the leaves can be tolerated by diabetics and so they are useful for sweetening tart fruit, fruit drinks and jellies etc.

The unripe seeds are tasty in fruit salads and chopped into ice-cream. The ripe ones, crushed, will sweeten fruit pies.

The root can be used raw in salads, cooked as a root vegetable and served with butter, left to cool and chopped into a salad—or candied.

Medicinal use: Tea made from the fresh leaves makes a pleasant tonic. The leaves do not dry well.

In the home: Extract the oil by crushing the seeds. Add the oil extracted to bought furniture polish.

TANSY (Bachelors' buttons)
Tanecetum vulgare/ Chrysanthemum vulgare

Family: Compositae
Parts used: flowers, leaves and roots

Tansy is a decorative perennial with 1 m/3 ft high round, ridged stems, dark-green finely divided aromatic leaves and clusters of small mustard-yellow flowers. It is happy in sun or light shade and will tolerate poor soil. It seeds freely and can be divided.

Culinary use: The gingery rosemary tasting leaves flavour savoury dishes.

Medicinal use: Disinfectant, insecticide, soothing

A poultice made from the bruised leaves will ease the pain of sprains and bruises.

The leaves contain a hormone and made into tea make a facewash with an exfoliant ability which gives the face a cleaner, fresher look. It must be used with care as it could irritate and the tea should not be taken internally.

In the home: Sprigs of tansy will keep away flies, fleas, moths and silverfish.

In the garden: Plant under fruit trees to repel pests.

TARRAGON
Artemesia dracunculus

Family: Compositae
Parts used: leaves

There are two types of tarragon, French and Russian—French has the better flavour—Russian is easier to grow. Tarragon grows 1metre/3feet tall, has thin, narrow aromatic leaves and tiny white unremarkable flowers and needs a light, dryish soil with sun for part of the day and winter protection against wind and rain. Propagation is by root division. The leaves do not dry well.

Culinary use: The clean sharp taste of the leaves enlivens savoury dishes. They should be added when the food is almost ready as long cooking spoils their taste. Chopped leaves can be sprinkled over soups, stews and cooked vegetables. Tarragon vinegar is good with salads.

Medicinal use: Aperitif, stomachic

Tea made from the leaves relieves wind, promotes appetite and eases rheumatic pain.

THYME
Thymus spp.

Family: Labiatae
Parts used: leaves

There are many different varieties of thyme, all with aromatic leaves and tiny white, pink or lilac flowers. They all like sun and a poorish soil. Propagation is by layering or division; seed can be tricky. Leaves are best picked for drying when the flowers are out.

All thymes have thin, narrow tough leaves which have powerful antiseptic and preservative properties. Some are creeping and low-growing, others make small bushes. All make splendid garden plants. Bees love them.

Culinary use: The leaves are used, fresh or dried, alone or in a bouquet garni to flavour savoury dishes, stuffings, sauces, pickles. Bruised leaves rubbed over a piece of meat will preserve it and give it a better flavour.

Medicinal use: Antiseptic, antispasmodic, deodorant, tonic

Tea from the leaves is good for chest ailments, nausea, the onset of migraine, sore throats and germs in general.

Leaves boiled up release their antiseptic oil. The liquid is good for bathing cuts and wounds.

Cosmetic use: Strong thyme tea, strained, is good to add to the bath water and as a hair rinse. Rubbed into the scalp it is said to stop hair falling out.

In the garden: It keeps away the cabbage-root fly.

UVA-URSI (Bearberry)
Arctostaphylos uva-ursi

Family: Ericaceae
Parts used: leaves

Uva-ursi is a perennial creeping groundcover with thick, flat, oval leaves and tiny white flowers which are followed by bright red berries. It grows in temperate parts of the world and likes a poor, gravelly soil in sun or shade. It has been used as a medical herb since the Middle Ages and the dried leaves are sold by herbalists all over the world.

Medicinal use: astringent, diuretic and for female complaints

Tea made from the leaves has a high tannin content and should only be taken as long as the troublesome condition lasts. Its main use is as a disinfectant for the kidneys and urinary tract and as a douche for leucorrhoea.

VALERIAN
Valeriana officinalis

Family: Valerianaceae
Parts used: roots

Valerian is a tall perennial with narrow, toothed, dark-green leaves that smell a bit like horse-radish, and clusters of little pink flowers growing in the leaf-axils at the top of the stems. It likes a rich moist soil and to have its head in the sun and its feet in the shade.

Propagation is by root division. Roots are not ready for drying until they are two years old. Drying must be slow and protection given against cats and rats which love it.

Medicinal use: anodyne, antispasmodic, nervine

Valerian provides an excellent sedative without side effects. It is good for epilepsy, hysteria, spasms, giddiness, migraine, breathlessness, palpitations, headache, menopausal miseries, sleeplessness, bladder gravel and wind.

The root should not be boiled. Leave a small piece of root to soak in water overnight and sweeten the solution with honey or pour 600 ml/1 pint boiling water over 30 g/l oz root, leave to cool and take in wineglassful doses every few hours. Dosage should not be too frequent or too strong.

VERBENA
Lippia citriodora

Family: Verbenaceae
Parts used: leaves

Verbena is a small deciduous shrub with pale green pointed lemon-scented leaves and pale lavender flower which grow in panicles at the end of the stems. It needs a good soil, warmth, shelter and regular trimming. Propagation is from heeled cuttings.

Pick leaves for drying at any time.

Culinary use: The chopped leaves can be used instead of lemon rind or for making a refreshing "tea".

Medicinal use: digestive, sedative
Tea made from the leaves is a gentle sedative, a stomach settler, and will help to clear mucus from the bronchial tubes and sinuses.

In the home: The dried leaves hold their scent well—use them in potpourri and to make scented sachets.

Caution: Large doses or prolonged use can cause internal irritation.

VERVAIN
Verbena officinalis

Family: Verbenaceae
Parts used: whole plant

This is the medicinal member of the verbena family. It does not look like lemon verbena and has different properties.

It is a hardy perennial, grows to 1 metre/3 feet high, wild, and on dry, chalky grassland. It has rough, heavily toothed leaves and spikes of pale mauve flowers It was the "magic" plant of the ancients. It foiled evil spirits and brought happiness back to abandoned lovers. Today it is appreciated for its medicinal properties.

The dried leaves are obtainable commercially.

Medicinal use: emetic, emmenogoguic, expectorant, nervine, sudorific, tonic, vermifuge

Vervain tea, taken in wineglassful doses, is good for headaches, colds, fevers, delayed menstruation, menstrual discomforts and scanty flow. It makes a good gargle when gums are unhealthy and the breath bad. It has such a pronounced effect on both nerves and liver it should be taken as soon as sickliness, shortage of energy, bloatedness and tearfulness and that "yellow" look become apparent.

Strong vervain tea helps the body to expel worms. A fat vervain poultice, fresh or dried, will relieve lumbago.

VIOLET
Viola odorata

Family: Violaceae
Parts used: leaves and flowers

The wild violet has adapted readily to cultivation. In the wild it has a single, small open-faced flower, violet-coloured and sweet-scented; in cultivation the flowers are either single or double and their colours range from deep purple, through pink to white and yellow.

Fragrance is variable and there are many varieties. The sweet violet likes a rich, moist soil and light shade with sun morning and evening. It increases willingly from runners.

Flowers and leaves can be picked for drying early in the year.

Culinary use: The flowers are edible fresh or candied.

Medicinal use: antiseptic, expectorant

Tea made from the leaves and flowers loosens chest phlegm and is good for whooping cough, nerves, headaches and insomnia and is gently laxative.

A warm poultice of crushed leaves can ease the pain of cracked nipples for nursing mothers.

In the home: The dried flowers give colour and scent to potpourri.

WITCH HAZEL (Winterbloom)
Hamamelis virginiana

Family: Hamamelidaceae
Parts used: bark and leaves

Witch hazel is a small shrub up to 4 m/13 ft in height, with smooth, greyish bark, dark green pointed leaves and stringy yellow flowers. It likes a cool climate, rich soil and moisture. It is not a decorative plant and since extract from its leaves and bark is readily available commercially it is not often found in the home garden.

Medicinal use: astringent, sedative, tonic
Witch hazel ointment will shrink piles and draw together wounds.

Cosmetic use: Witch hazel extract is bought for use as a facial astringent. It should be used diluted.

Caution: Tinctures made from the leaves and bark may cause allergic reactions.

WOOD BETONY (Bishop's wort)
Stachys officinalis

Family: Labiatae
Parts used: whole plant

This herb grows wild in temperate parts of the world and looks like other members of the nettle family. The stem is tall and hairy, the leaves dark-green and toothed; the reddish-purple flowers are splotched and grow in spikes.

The fresh herb should not be used, only the bought dried leaves.

Medicinal use: alterative, astringent, tonic

It is mostly used in conjunction with other herbs as a digestive or sedative.

WOODRUFF (Waldmeister tea)
Asperula odorata

Family: Rubiaceae
Parts used: whole plant

Woodruff has small shiny leaves, hooked around the edges, tiny, sweet-scented, star-shaped flowers which grow in floppy whorls at the top of the short stems. It grows wild in temperate parts of the world but can be cultivated. Propagation is by root division.

Medicinal use: diuretic, tonic

Tea made from the chopped herb tastes clean and sweet and is a tonic.

WORMWOOD (Old woman)
Artemesia absinthium

Family: Compositae
Parts used: whole plant

There are many varieties of this bushy perennial. All are decorative and are much used in "grey" gardens. There are upright and creeping types—all have silvery, feathery leaves and small, yellow, daisy-faced flowers which grow on short stalks from the leaf-axils.

Medicinal use: anthelmintic, disinfectant, febrifuge, stomachic, tonic

Tea made from the chopped flowers and leaves has the bitter taste of absinth. It stimulates the appetite, the liver and the female reproductive organs. It speeds the elimination of food and excess water and expels worms.

In the home: Wash dogs in wormwood tea to get rid of fleas. Moths and mosquitoes don't like it either.

YARROW (Soldiers' woundwort, Knight's milfoil)
Achillea millefolium

Family: Compositae
Parts used: whole plant

Yarrow grows to 30 cm/12 inches high, has strong, angular stems growing from a creeping rhizome root, darkgreen, ferny, very finely divided leaves and dense umbels of pinky-white flowers. It grows wild but there are many cultivated varieties, mostly lower-growing and with pink, white or yellow flowers. It is an excellent garden plant—it gives strength to its neighbours.

Culinary use: The leaves taste peppery and are used in salad or as a garnish.

Medicinal use: astringent, carminative, diaphoretic, tonic

Tea made from the leaves and flowers will invigorate the liver and kidneys, regulate the bowels and the menstrual flow and cleanse the blood. It is a good wound herb and is often prescribed homeopathically for unrelenting nosebleeds, undue bleeding after childbirth or tooth extraction, and bleeding piles.

Cosmetic use: Yarrow tea, used as a facewash, will dry greasy skin.

INDEX